TIMESAVER CROSS-CURRICULAR ENGLISH ACTIVITIES

Teacher's reference key

A small clock on each page tells you approximately how long each activity should take.

Contents

Flags

Read the key and colour the flags.
Can you write the correct country under each flag?

Key	
1 red	**5** green
2 yellow	**6** blue
3 white	**7** orange
4 black	

South Africa   **Sweden**   **Ireland**
Pakistan   **Jamaica**   **Canada**

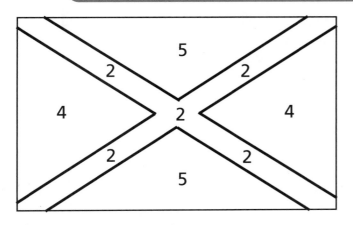

A ....

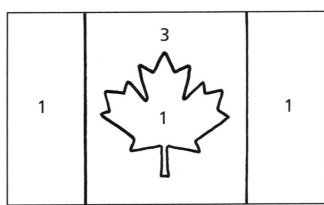

B ....

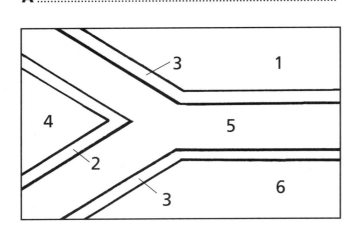

C ....

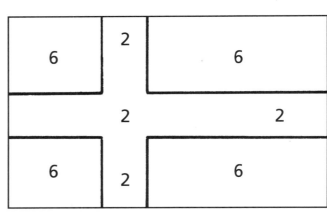

D ....

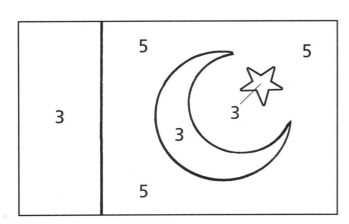

E ....

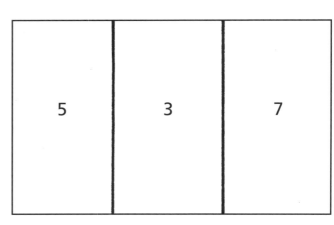

F ....

Regions of the World
Where does it come from?
The food we eat comes from all over the world.
Different regions export different kinds of food around the world.

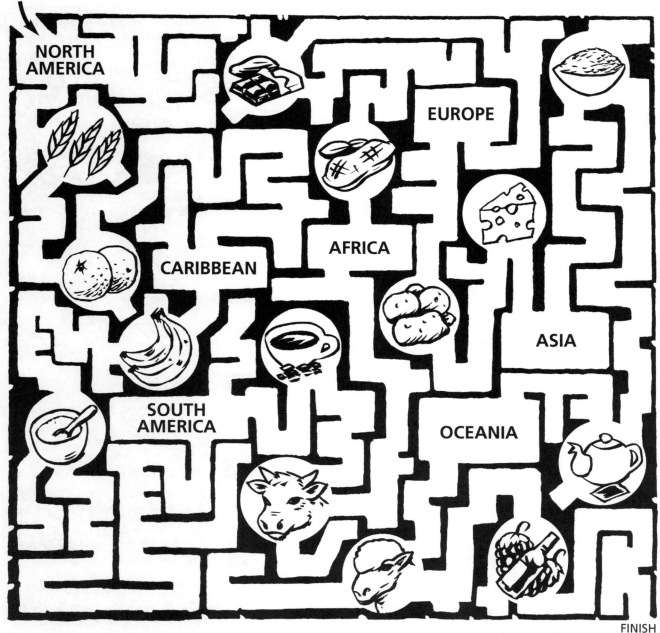

START HERE

FINISH

Find your way through the maze. After each region of the world there are two types of food or drink. These are two of the major food products from that region. Write the names of the food and drink next to the correct regions.

bananas	beef	cheese
cocoa	coffee	lamb	~~oranges~~
peanuts	potatoes	rice
sugar	tea	~~wheat~~	wine

1 North America .....*wheat*..... .....*oranges*.....

2 Caribbean ....

3 South America ....

4 Africa ....

5 Europe ....

6 Asia ....

7 Oceania ....

Ecosystems
What is it? What does it eat?
Write the name of each animal next to its picture. Use the words in the box.
Then match the animals with their food.

mountain goat   dolphin   rabbit   ~~penguin~~   squirrel   parrot   alligator   scorpion   giraffe

1 ....penguin.............

2 ....

3 ....

4 ....

5 ....

6 ....

7 ....

8 ....

9 ....

a insects and spiders

b fish, birds, turtles and small mammals

c leaves from trees

d fish and squid

e nuts and seeds

f herbs, bark and vegetables

g grass and all mountain plants

h seeds and fruit

i fish

Ecosystems
Where does it live?
Write the name of each animal from page 6 under the picture of its habitat.

Tropical forest

1 ....

Ocean

2 ....

Polar regions

3 ....

River

4 ....

Temperate forest

5 ....

Desert

6 ....

Savanna

7 ....

Mountains

8 ....

Grassland

9 ....

Recycling

What is it made of?

All the things we use come from the Earth. We can recycle a lot of the things we use.
Look at this rubbish. Do you know what everything is made of?

Find the words in the wordsearch → ↓. Then write the words in the correct place in the list.

1 a battery ☐
~~metal and~~ *chemicals*

2 a jam jar ☐
....

3 an old T-shirt ☐
....

4 a magazine ☐
....

5 a yoghurt pot ☐
....

6 a food can ☐
....

7 a cereal packet ☐
....

8 an old jumper ☐
....

9 an orange crate ☐
....

P	C	L	A	V	W	O	O	L
L	H	I	M	E	T	A	L	C
A	E	D	O	G	C	E	P	O
S	M	U	E	E	O	N	A	W
T	I	C	A	T	T	G	P	O
I	C	K	B	A	T	O	E	O
C	A	R	D	B	O	A	R	D
P	L	A	Y	L	N	T	E	N
I	S	I	A	E	V	A	L	P
G	L	A	S	S	P	F	O	X

**Look at the words
in the exercise again.**

**Tick (✔) the things
that you can recycle.**

**Cross (✗) the things
that you can't recycle.**

Geographical Features

Some features in our landscape are natural and some things are made by humans. Look at the picture and write the names of the features of the landscape. Use the words in the box.

| bridge | coast | farm | forest | hill | island | lake | marsh |
| | | mountain | river | road | sea | town | wind farm |

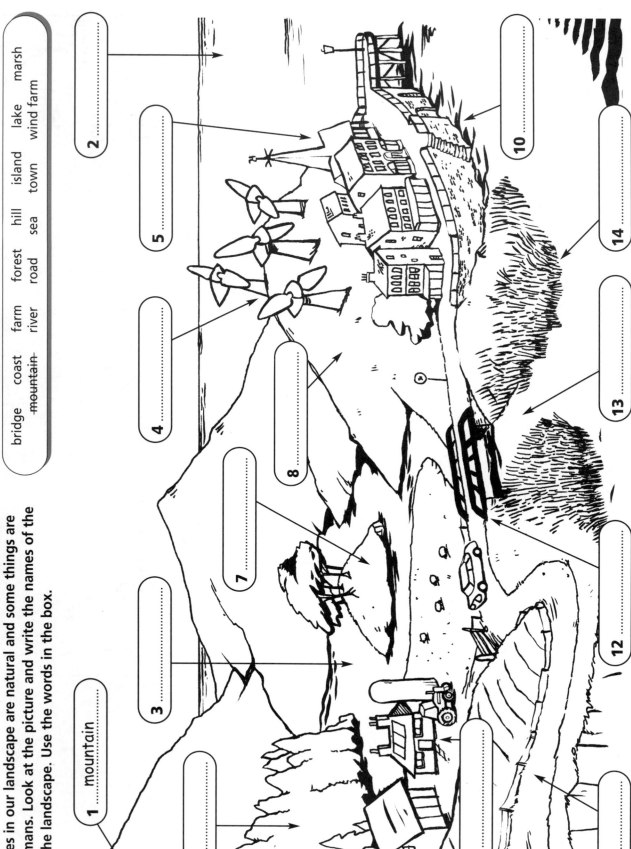

1 ___mountain___

2 ....

3 ....

4 ....

5 ....

6 ....

7 ....

8 ....

9 ....

10 ....

11 ....

12 ....

13 ....

14 ....

World Time Zones

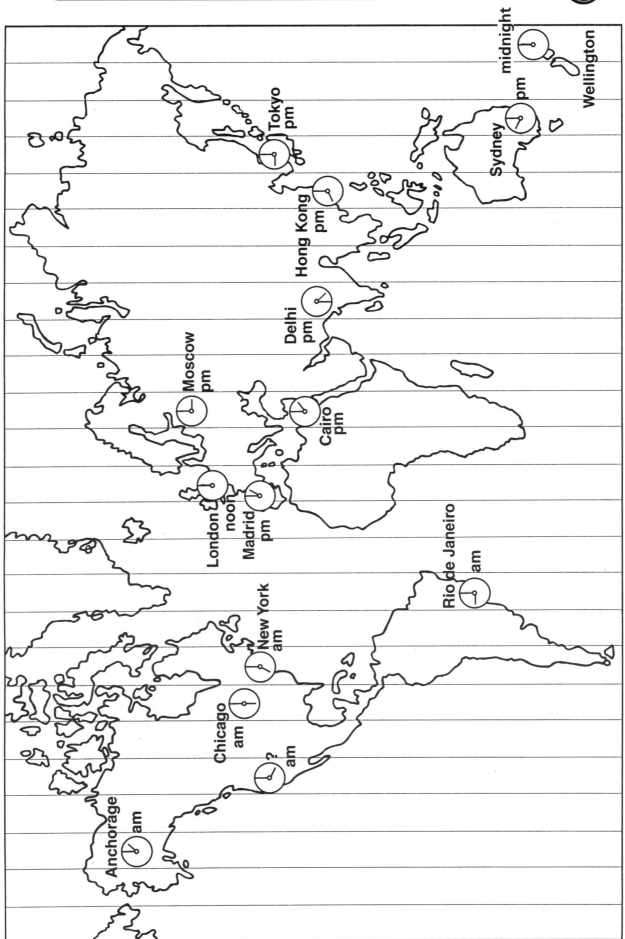

World Time Zones

Look at the times on the map of the world.
Complete the sentences with the names of the cities and the times.

When it's twelve noon in London, it's ...

1 ....seven...... am in New York.

2 one pm in ....

3 .... am in Rio de Janeiro.

4 .... thirty pm in Delhi.

5 two am in ....

6 six am in ....

7 twelve midnight in ....

8 three pm in ....

9 .... pm in Hong Kong.

10 ten pm in ....

11 two pm in ....

12 nine pm in ....

Complete the crossword with the words from the exercise above to find the name of
the mystery city.

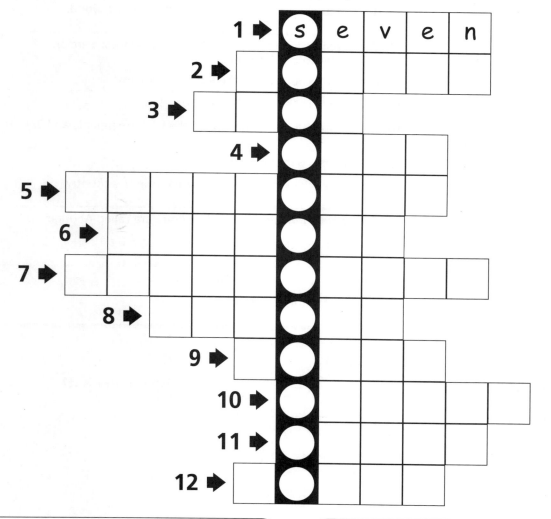

1 The mystery city is ....

2 The time in this city is ....

Country Fact File

Unscramble the letters to find the names of the countries. Read the two facts about each country.
One fact is true and one is false. Write *True* or *False* next to each sentence.
Correct the errors in the false sentences to make them true.

Russia .... **A** SURISA	**1** This is the smallest country in the world.　False This is the biggest country in the world. **2** The capital city is Moscow.　True
.... **B** HINAC	**3** This country is in north America. **4** It's got the largest population in the world.
.... **C** UNTAISI	**5**　This country is in north Africa. **6** Its coast is on the Pacific Ocean.
.... **D** GENTARAIN	**7**　The capital city is Rio de Janeiro. **8** This country's name means land of silver.
.... **E** AAANCD	**9**　Most people in this country speak French or English. **10** This country has got the shortest coastline in the world.
.... **F** TADNSZWIELR	**11**　The people in this country speak four languages: German, French, Italian and Romansch. **12** Most of this country is in the Rocky Mountains.
.... **G** COMIXE	**13**　The people in this country speak German. **14** This country has got borders with the USA, Guatemala and Belize.
.... **H** YANKE	**15**　This country is in the Arctic Circle. **16** You can see lions, giraffes and elephants in this country.
.... **I** ASTARAILU	**17**　The original inhabitants of this country are called Aborigines. **18** Most of this country is forest.
.... **J** LAPEN	**19**　This country is surrounded by sea. **20** This country is in the Himalayas.

**Colour the numbers of the
true sentences to find the
shape of a country.**

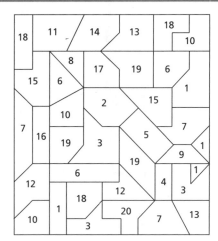

Which country is it?

— — — — —

Migration

People always move: from the countryside to the city, from one region to another region and from one country to another country. This is called *migration*.

Moving out of a country or region is called *emigration*.
Moving into a country or region is called *immigration*.

Why do people migrate?
1 There is high unemployment.
2 There are a lot of their friends or family members in the new country.
3 There are good schools and universities.
4 There is a good climate.
5 There is a war.
6 There are religious or political problems.
7 There are a lot of jobs.
8 There is a natural disaster, e.g., a flood or an earthquake.

Write the number of each sentence in the correct box.

Reasons to emigrate from a region
1

Reasons to immigrate into a region
2

Large cities attract people from many different places.
The people living in London speak 307 different languages. Can you find the nationalities of some of the groups of people who live in London? Read the clues and place the blocks in the grid to find 17 different nationalities. All the words go across. ▶

Clue												
from South Asia; from east Asia	■	I	N	D	I	A						
from west Africa; from the Middle East	N	I	G	E	R	I						
from southern Europe; from western Europe	■	T	U	R	K	I						
from eastern Europe; from north Africa												
from western Europe												
from South America; from southern Europe												
from the Caribbean; from south-east Asia												
from south Asia												
from east Africa; from western Europe												

Blocks:

I	S	H
O	R	T
Z	I	L

■	E	G
U	G	U
I	A	N

H	I	N
I	R	A
F	R	E

A	I	■
I	■	■
I	S	H

■	J	A
■	■	B
E	T	H

N	■	C
A	N	■
S	H	■

■	T	H
E	S	H
■	I	R

I	A	N
■	■	■
E	E	K

P	O	L
■	■	P
B	R	A

M	A	I
A	N	G
I	O	P

C	A	N
L	A	D
I	A	N

European Weather

This is the weather forecast for Europe on 21st May. Read the weather forecast.

- In Bergen, there will be sunshine and some showers. The temperature will be twelve degrees.

- Murmansk will be sunny and mild with a temperature of fifteen degrees.

- Stockholm will be cloudy with some sunshine. It will be nineteen degrees Celsius.

- Moscow will be warm and cloudy with some sunshine and a temperature of twenty-two degrees.

- London will be rainy and mild, with a temperature of seventeen degrees.

- There will be thunderstorms in Paris and the temperature will be seventeen degrees.

- It will be cloudy and warm in Madrid, with a temperature of twenty-five degrees.

- Berlin will have rain and a temperature of eighteen degrees.

- Warsaw will be rainy and the temperature will be eighteen degrees.

- In Budapest, it will be warm. The temperature will be twenty-one degrees. There will be sunshine and some showers.

- Rome will be warm and sunny with a temperature of twenty-four degrees.

- There will be a mixture of sunshine and cloud in Athens and it will be twenty-four degrees Celsius.

- Ankara will be sunny and hot: twenty-seven degrees Celsius.

Some of the symbols and temperatures on the weather map are wrong. Circle the mistakes.

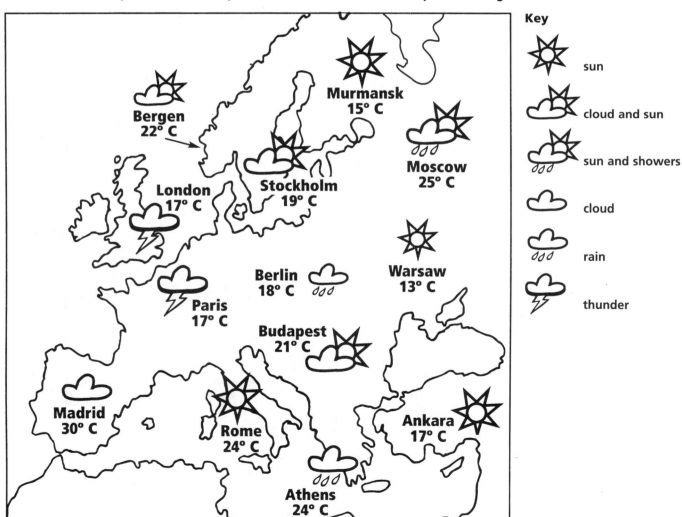

Town Planning
Design your own town!
Read the rules.

Rules

1 The power station must not be near to the houses or blocks of flats.

2 The school must be near the housing estate.

3 The park and small shops must be near the houses and flats.

4 The hospital and school must not be close to the industries.

5 The town hall must be in the town centre.

6 The supermarket must be near the department store.

7 All the buildings and the park must be next to roads.

8 Your town must contain all of these buildings:

Residential buildings	Industries	Recreational buildings	Shops	Civic buildings
2 blocks of flats (2 x 2) 1 housing estate (4 x 4)	1 factory (4 x 3) 1 power station (6 x 4)	1 cinema (2 x 3) 1 sports club (2 x 4) 1 park (3 x 3)	1 supermarket (3 x 3) 1 department store (4 x 3) 5 small shops (1 x 1)	1 hospital (3 x 3) 1 school (2 x 3) 1 town hall (3 x 3) 1 police station (2 x 3)

The numbers show you how big the buildings are. For example:

A block of flats is 2 x 2.

The department store is 4 x 3.

or

Design your town on the grid. The roads are shaded grey.

You can place two more buildings in your town. Decide which buildings you want and how big they are.

World Travel

Kirsty and Tim have travelled all over the world.
Complete the questions. Use the past participle of the verbs.

Have you ever...

1 (hear) .....heard..... the bagpipes? ☑

2 (fly) .... over the Grand Canyon in a helicopter? ☐

3 (ride) .... an elephant? ☐

4 (see) .... the Eiffel Tower? ☐

5 (swim) .... in the Dead Sea? ☐

6 (drive) .... across the Sahara Desert? ☐

7 (take) .... a photo of Uluru (Ayers Rock)? ☐

8 (buy) .... a postcard of the Pyramids? ☐

9 (eat) .... paella? ☐

10 (meet) .... a sumo wrestler? ☐

The answers to the questions are in the wrong order.
Read the answers and put a tick (✔) in the boxes next to the things that Kirsty and Tim have done.

Yes, in Spain.

No, we've never been to France.

Yes, in Japan.

No, we've never been to Israel.

~~Yes, in Scotland.~~

No, we've never been to the USA

Yes, we spent two months in Australia.

No, we've never been to Egypt.

No, we've never been to India.

Yes, in Algeria.

Now, tick (✔) the things that you have done.

Earthquakes

Earthquakes cause destruction and death in many parts of the world.
The Richter scale measures the size and strength of earthquakes.
Can you match the descriptions with the numbers on the Richter scale?
Write the letters in the correct box.

A Most buildings are destroyed.
B The earthquake is too small to notice. Nothing moves.
C It is difficult to stand.

D Tree branches break.
E Liquid spills.
F Loose objects move.

Richter scale | Description

1–2.9
3–3.9
4–4.9
5–5.9
6–6.9
7–9

After the earthquake

There are lots of important things to do after an earthquake. Can you put these sentences in order? Write 1 next to the first thing to do, 2 next to the second thing to do, and so on.

Provide emergency medical assistance. ☐

Repair communications. ☐

Rescue people who are trapped under buildings. ☐

Start rebuilding houses. ☐

Find out how bad the damage is. ☐

Start an earthquake education programme. ☐

Provide emergency food, water and shelter. ☐

Demolish dangerous buildings. ☐

Tourism

Tourism is the fastest growing industry in the world. Every day, more and more people from developed countries travel to developing countries, such as India and Kenya.

Read the questions and tick (✔) the correct answers. There is more than one correct answer to each question. The incorrect sentences are also gramatically incorrect.
Correct the use of *a lot of, many* and *much* in the incorrect sentences.

1 Why is the tourist industry in developing countries growing?

B ☐ People in developing countries ~~have much~~ money for holidays.
haven't got a lot of

T ☑ People want to see **a lot of** different countries.

C ☐ Not **much** developing countries welcome tourists.

H ☐ People in developed countries have **much** more leisure time than they used to.

A ☐ There are **a lot of** cheap holidays available.

2 What are the advantages of tourism to local people in developing countries?

M ☐ Often there isn't **many** water because the tourists use it all.

I ☐ Tourism creates **a lot of** jobs for local people.

O ☐ Most of the money from tourism goes to the tour operators, so not **much** local people benefit.

E ☐ Some tourists don't show **many** respect for the local culture.

L ☐ Tourists spend **a lot of** money while they are on holiday.

3 What are the environmental disadvantages of international tourism?

A ☐ Aeroplanes cause **a lot of** pollution.

N ☐ There aren't **many** wild places left in the world and tourist developments are destroying them.

U ☐ **Much** tourists like taking photos of wild animals.

D ☐ Tourists create **a lot of** rubbish.

S ☐ Sunbathing and swimming don't create **many** pollution.

The letters next to the correct answers spell the name of a country that is popular with tourists.

The popular holiday country is __T__ __ __ __ __ __ __ __

Water

This crossword is all about water.
Read the clues and complete the crossword. Use the words in the box.

bed   sea   ice   lake   tide   land   melt   acid   ~~sand~~   snow
deep   well   fresh   rains   waves   stream   clouds   vapour   drains
glacier   estuary   condenses   waterfall   reservoir   evaporates

Across (↓)

2 A _ _ _ _ _ _ _ is a large river of ice that moves slowly over the land.

5 The wind makes _ _ _ _ _ when it blows on the sea.

7 _ _ _ _ falls from clouds when it is very cold.

9 The bottom of the Mediterranean Sea is 5,000 metres _ _ _ _ .

11 When snow and ice _ _ _ _ they become water again.

13 70% of the Earth's surface is water and 30% is _ _ _ _ .

15 A _ _ _ _ _ _ _ _ _ is an artificial lake that collects water for humans.

16 In deserts it hardly ever _ _ _ _ _ .

19 A _ _ _ _ is a deep hole for collecting water from under the ground.

21 _ _ _ is frozen water.

23 Pollution from factories mixes with vapour in the air to make _ _ _ _ rain.

24 A _ _ _ _ _ _ is a small river.

25 The bottom of a river is called the river _ _ _

Down (↓)

1 You find _ _ _ _ on the beach. It is made of tiny particles of rock.

3 When water vapour rises it _ _ _ _ _ _ _ _ _ to make clouds.

4 An _ _ _ _ _ _ _ is a large river close to the sea.

6 Another word for steam is water _ _ _ _ _ _ .

8 When a river goes over a cliff, it's called a _ _ _ _ _ _ _ _ _ .

10 When the sun shines on the sea, the water _ _ _ _ _ _ _ _ _ _ .

12 Water in the air forms _ _ _ _ _ _ .

14 In towns, rainwater goes into _ _ _ _ _ _ .

17 The water in the sea is salty. The water in rivers and lakes is _ _ _ _ _ .

18 The moon's gravity on the sea causes a high and a low _ _ _ _ every day.

20 A _ _ _ _ is a large pool of fresh water.

22 Rivers flow into the _ _ _ .

Multiplication

Do the multiplication problems and write the answers in the puzzle grid.
Some numbers are already in the grid. Can you write clues for these numbers?

	A 1	8		**B** 6	**C** 4	
D			**E**		2	**F**
	G					
				H		
I 9		**J**				
K 5	**L**			**M** 5	4	
	N 9	9		**O**		

Across (▶)

A Two multiplied by nine

B ....

D Fifteen multiplied by five

E One hundred and fifty-three multiplied by twenty-five

G Seven hundred and fifty-four multiplied by twelve

J One hundred and one multiplied by forty-four

K Four hundred and sixty-nine multiplied by twelve

M ....

N ....

O Twenty-three multiplied by four

Down (▼)

A Thirty-seven multiplied by forty-three

B Forty-three multiplied by sixteen

C ....

E Thirty-two multiplied by eight multiplied by one hundred and thirty-three

F Ten multiplied by five

H Ninety-two multiplied by eighty-one

I ....

J One hundred and forty-three multiplied by three

L Twenty-three multiplied by three

You can do the multiplication sums here

2 x 9 = 18

Averages

This is a survey of favourite sports. The pupils in four classes chose one sport.
There are 30 pupils in each class.

Can you find the average for each sport? Complete the table.

Example: 3 + 6 + 3 + 4 = 16, *16 ÷ 4 = 4*

Sports Survey

My favourite sport is ...	Class A	Class B	Class C	Class D	Average
running	3	6	3	4	4
swimming	5	7	7	5	
tennis	4	4	3	1	
hockey	2	2	3	1	
football	7	5	2	6	
volleyball	6	3	6	5	
gymnastics	2	1	3	2	
basketball	1	2	3	6	
TOTAL	30	30	30	30	(average) 30

Look at the table in exercise 1 and draw the bar chart.

Favourite Sports

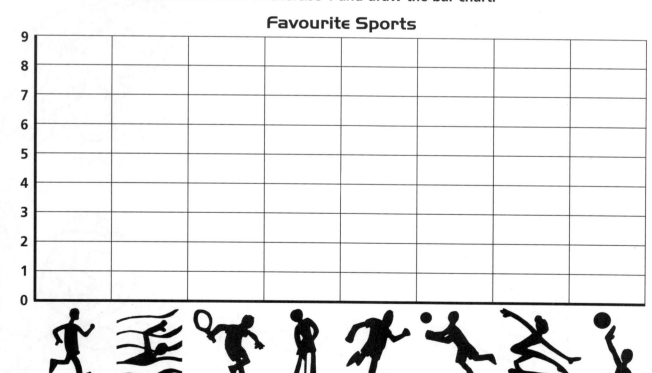

On average, which is the most popular sport? ....

Fractions

The king is writing his will. He wants to leave 20,000 gold coins to his family.
He wants each person to receive a fraction of the money.
Unfortunately, he is not very good at maths. Can you help him to write his will?

Put the fractions in the correct order in King Harold's will. Write the biggest fraction first and the smallest last.

$$\frac{3}{8} \quad \frac{1}{16} \quad \frac{1}{8} \quad \frac{3}{16} \quad \frac{1}{4}$$

The last Will and Testament of King Harold

I leave 20,000 gold coins to my family.

(1) ...... $\frac{3}{8}$ ...... *to my son, Percival*

(2) .... *to my wife, Bertha*

(3) .... *to my daughter, Charlotte*

(4) .... *to my brother, John*

(5) .... *to my mother, Mary*

How many gold coins does each person receive?

Write the amount under each person.

1 Prince John
2,500 gold coins

2 Princess Charlotte

3 Queen Mary

4 Queen Bertha

5 Prince Percival

Coordinates

**Look at the places on the grid. Write the names of the places next to the coordinates.
You need to use the words in the key.**

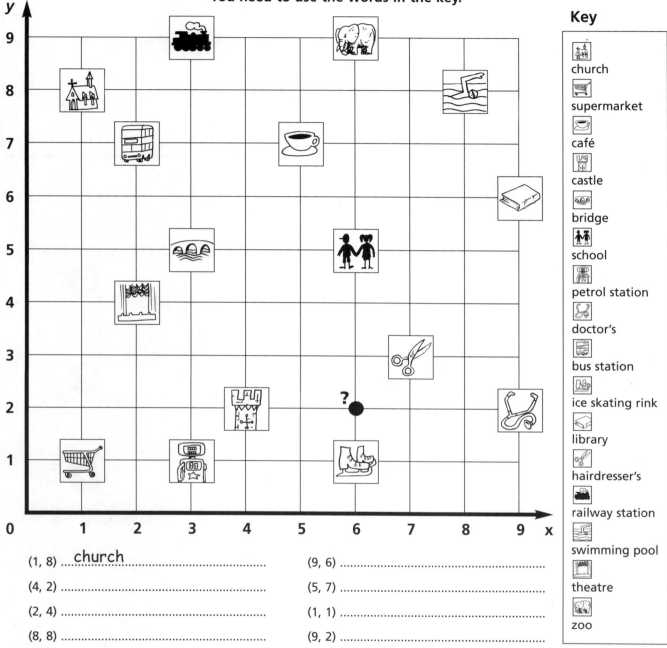

Key

church
supermarket
café
castle
bridge
school
petrol station
doctor's
bus station
ice skating rink
library
hairdresser's
railway station
swimming pool
theatre
zoo

(1, 8) ....church..............................

(4, 2) ....

(2, 4) ....

(8, 8) ....

(9, 6) ....

(5, 7) ....

(1, 1) ....

(9, 2) ....

I'm going to (6,2).
Find out which place is at (6,2).
Read the instructions
and join the coordinates.
The letter you find is the
first letter of the place
I'm going to.

Join the **bridge** to the **bus station**.
Join the **petrol station** to the **ice skating rink**.
Join the **railway station** to the **zoo**.
Join the **hairdresser's** to the **school**.
Join the **bus station** to the **railway station**.
Join the **ice skating rink** to the **hairdresser's**.
Join the **school** to the **bridge**.

Which place is at (6,2)?

museum ☐   bank ☐   hotel ☐   shopping centre ☐   cinema ☐

Division Directions

Do the sums on the map in the correct order. The answer of each sum is the number of your next direction. Follow the directions to find your way through the streets.

Where do you finish? Tick the letter where you finish.

1 Go straight on. ☐
2 Turn left and walk to the first turning on the right. ☐
3 Turn left up Old Street and walk to the crossroads. ☐
4 Turn left up Main Street and walk to the first turning on your left. ☐
5 Turn left and walk to the second turning on your right. ☐
6 Turn right and walk a short way. ☐
7 Turn right up Short Street and walk to the crossroads. ☐
8 Turn right up Castle Street and walk to the first turning on your right. ☐
9 Turn right and walk to the end of the road. ☐
10 Turn right and walk to the end of the road. ☐

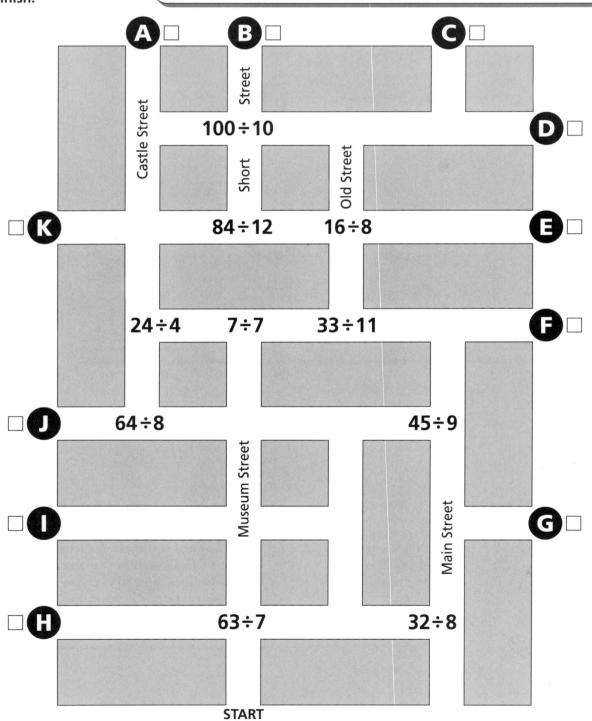

Factors and Multiples

Read the sentences and work out each number.

> **Factors**
> For example: 1, 2, 4, 8 and 16 are all factors of 16.
>
> **Multiples**
> For example: 3, 6, 9 and 12 are all multiples of 3.
>
> **Prime numbers**
> Prime numbers have exactly two factors. For example: 3, 11 and 19 are prime numbers.

A It's smaller than 100.
It's bigger than 50.
It's a multiple of 10.
It's a factor of 120.

> 60

E It's an even number.
It's a factor of 32.
It's bigger than 2.
It's smaller than 8.

B It's a prime number.
It's a factor of 28.
It's bigger than 3.
It's smaller than 10.

F It's a multiple of 3.
It's bigger than 6.
It's smaller than 20.
It's a factor of 48.

C It's bigger than 11.
It's smaller than 50.
It's a factor of 90.
It's a multiple of 10.

G It's bigger than 40.
It's smaller than 70.
It's a multiple of 13.
It's a factor of 364.

D It's a multiple of 8.
It's a factor of 72.
It's smaller than 30.
It's bigger than 20.

Read the clues and write the correct number.
The numbers are the answers from the questions in the exercise above.

a) The number of minutes in an hour. 60 ....

b) The number of hours in a day. ....

c) The number of days in a week. ....

d) The number of days in June. ....

e) The number of weeks in a year. ....

f) The number of months in a year. ....

g) The number of seasons in a year. ....

Ordering numbers

These people live in the same block of flats. Can you find out where they all live? Put each set of numbers in order, starting with the smallest, and make a sentence. The sentences are all clues about where the people live. Write the people's names in the correct flats.

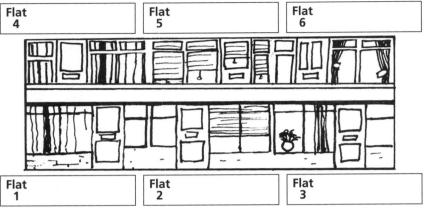

Flat 4	Flat 5	Flat 6

Flat 1	Flat 2	Flat 3

Sally Preston, Claire Sanchez and Mark Osborne | the Andersons | the Peels | June Willis | James Nichols | Candice and George Sweet

1

870	329	943	812	286	538	364	635	157	491
flat	couple	four	in	young	baby	and	live	the	their

157	286								
The	young								

2

1.573	7.196	0.783	0.536	0.0065	75.12	1.742	6.571	56.23	3.184	0.175	0.035	31.48	0.563
young	a	the	lady	between	four	man	is	of	there	elderly	the	family	and

3

5.876	5.765	5.867	8.756	7.586	7.856	8.675	6.857
couple	the	middle-aged	man	above	the	young	live

4

−5.76	6.92	−8.29	−7.51	9.63	−7.051	2.45	1.32	−1.82	0	0.84	−9.35
their	three	young	couple	flatmates	and	the	to	baby	live	next	the

Equivalent Fractions

Yesterday, somebody stole the king's crown. What were the king's servants doing yesterday?
Find the equivalent fractions for each person and make sentences with the words.

Equivalent fractions have the
same value. For example, these
fractions are all equivalent:

$$\frac{1}{2} = \frac{2}{4} = \frac{3}{6} = \frac{4}{8} \ldots$$

1

$$\frac{2}{3}$$

The jester was ....
....

2

$$\frac{5}{8}$$

The cook was ....
....

3

$$\frac{2}{5}$$

The laundry maid was ....
....

4

$$\frac{1}{5}$$

The butler was ....
....

5

$$\frac{4}{7}$$

The coachman was ....
....

6

$$\frac{3}{4}$$

The kitchen maid was ....
....

$\frac{8}{20}$ the	$\frac{20}{32}$ cakes	$\frac{4}{6}$ singing	$\frac{4}{20}$ the	$\frac{20}{35}$ horses	$\frac{5}{25}$ crown	$\frac{6}{8}$ washing
$\frac{8}{14}$ feeding	$\frac{21}{28}$ floor	$\frac{15}{24}$ some	$\frac{10}{15}$ a	$\frac{6}{15}$ ironing	$\frac{20}{30}$ song
$\frac{10}{16}$ baking	$\frac{12}{16}$ the	$\frac{14}{35}$ clothes	$\frac{40}{70}$ the	$\frac{2}{10}$ stealing

Who stole the king's crown?   It was the ....

Maths Millionaire

Are you a maths millionaire? Answer as many questions as you can,
then ask your teacher for the answers.
In each section, the questions increase in difficulty.
You score the points for the most difficult question that you answer correctly.

	50,000 points	**100,000 points**	**150,000 points**	**200,000 points**
Percentages %	What is 10 per cent of 50? a) 3 b) 5 c) 10	What is 30 per cent of 120? a) 24 b) 30 c) 36	What is 58 per cent of 360? a) 182.6 b) 208.8 c) 214.6	Last year there were 520 pupils in a school. This year there are 25 per cent more pupils. How many pupils are there now? a) 650 b) 780 c) 800
Fractions $\frac{1}{2}$	What is $\frac{1}{7} + \frac{3}{7}$? a) $\frac{2}{7}$ b) $\frac{4}{7}$ c) $\frac{6}{7}$	Which fraction is equivalent to $\frac{3}{24}$? a) $\frac{1}{6}$ b) $\frac{1}{7}$ c) $\frac{1}{8}$	What is $\frac{4}{5} \div \frac{2}{5}$? a) $\frac{2}{5}$ b) $1\frac{1}{5}$ c) 2	There are 416 pupils in a school. 208 pupils are older than 14. What fraction is this? a) $\frac{4}{8}$ c) $\frac{3}{4}$ b) $\frac{6}{8}$
Number sequences 1 2 3 4 ...	Which number is next? 1 3 5 7 9 a) 11 b) 12 c) 13	Which number is next? 4 8 16 32 64 a) 96 b) 112 c) 128	Which number is next? 0 3 8 15 24 a) 30 b) 31 c) 35	Which number is next? 2 5 11 23 47 a) 92 b) 95 c) 101
Fractions, percentages and decimals $\frac{1}{2}$ = 0.5 = 50%	Which number is the biggest? a) $\frac{1}{2}$ b) 0.25 c) 30%	Which number is the biggest? a) $\frac{7}{10}$ b) 0.75 c) 7%	Which number is the biggest? a) $\frac{17}{20}$ b) 0.83 c) 86%	Which number is the biggest? a) $\frac{4}{7}$ b) $\frac{3}{5}$ c) 0.592
Mental arithmetic	What is 37 + 63? a) 90 b) 100 c) 110	What is 127 – 35? a) 82 b) 92 c) 102	What is 64 ÷ 8? a) 8 b) 12 c) 16	What is 16 x 18? a) 168 b) 246 c) 288

Percentages

It's the January sales. All the price tags show the original prices.
Work out the sale prices. Then write the prices on the posters in the shop windows.

Example: There is 50% off the dresses at Super Shop.
First work out the reduction. *50% of £35 is: 50 ÷ 100 x £35 = 0.5 x £35 = £17.50*
Then subtract the reduction from the original price. *£35 – £17.50 = £17.50*
The dresses at Super Shop are now £17.50.

£25 £36 £100

£36 **SALE 50% OFF**

1 Dresses ....£17.50.......
2 Jackets ....
3 T-shirts ....
4 Jumpers ....

cool clothes
MEGA SALE 25% OFF EVERYTHING

£60 £32 £16 £40

5 Shoes ....
6 Jeans ....
7 Jackets ....
8 T-shirts ....

GARAGE
JANUARY SALE   30% OFF EVERYTHING

£25 £20 £30 £65

 9 Jumpers ....
10 Dresses ....
11 Skirts ....
12 Coats ....

first fashion
BIG SALE! 20% OFF 20% OFF 20% OFF

13 Shoes ....
14 T-shirts ....
15 Jeans ....
16 Jumpers ....

£25 £12.50 £40 £27.50

Look at the posters and write *True* or *False*.

a Jackets are cheaper at Cool Clothes than at Supershop. ....True.....

b First Fashion has got the cheapest jumpers. ....

c Super Shop has got the cheapest T-shirts. ....

d Jeans are cheaper at Cool Clothes than at First Fashion. ....

e Dresses are cheaper at Super Shop than at Garage. ....

f Shoes are cheaper at Cool Clothes than at First Fashion. ....

Work out the sale prices here
25 ÷ 100 = 0.25 x 60 = 15
60 - 15 = 45

Cubes

All these shapes can be folded to make cubes.
Imagine the shapes when they are folded into
cubes. Which cubes will have opposite words
on opposite sides of the cubes? Make the
cubes to check your answers.

Example:
A – yes (fast – slow; short – long; sad – happy)

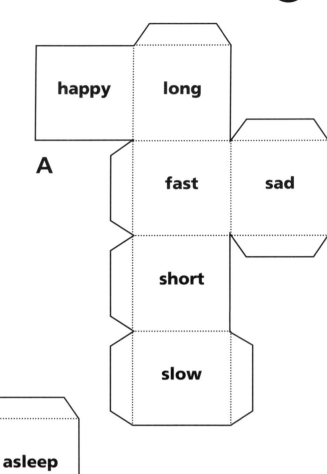

A

| happy | long |
| | fast | sad |
| short |
| slow |

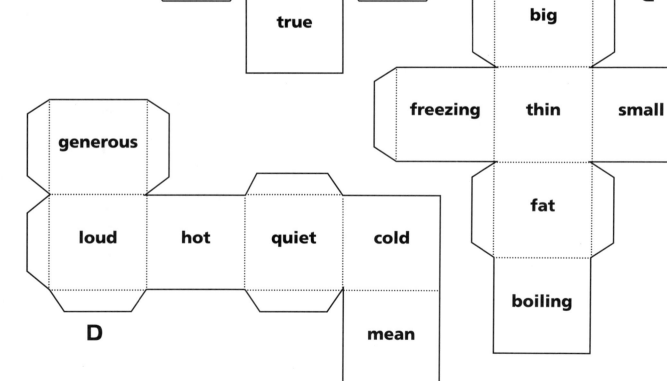

B

awake | dry
false | wet | asleep
true

C

big
freezing | thin | small
fat
boiling

D

generous
loud | hot | quiet | cold
mean

Cubes

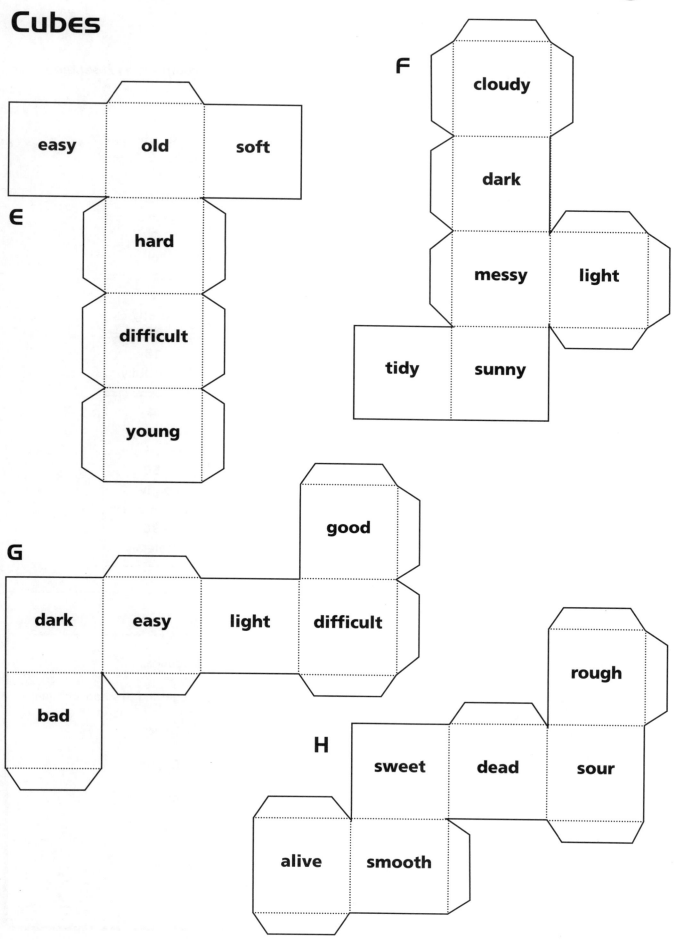

E

| easy | old | soft |

hard

difficult

young

F

cloudy

dark

messy | light

tidy | sunny

G

| dark | easy | light | difficult |

good

bad

H

rough

| sweet | dead | sour |

| alive | smooth |

Negative Numbers

Adrian is good at some things and bad at others.
Do the calculations with negative numbers and find the adverb to complete each sentence.

−1 + 2 =
Adrian solves maths problems very

1	3
quickly	slowly

−6 + 6 =
Adrian writes very

−12	0
neatly	untidily

4 − 7 =
Adrian speaks French very

11	−3
badly	well

−6 − 4 =
Adrian sings

−10	−2
terribly	sweetly

−11 + 7 =
Adrian draws

−4	−18
messily	beautifully

−7 x − 2 =
Adrian plays tennis

−14	14
gracefully	clumsily

−10 x 5 =
Adrian gets to school

50	−50
late	early

−12 x − 3 =
Adrian does his English homework

36	−36
carefully	carelessly

**Now complete
Adrian's school report.
What is he *good at*
and what is he *bad at*?
Fill in the gaps.**

School Report

1 Adrian is .... sports.

2 Adrian is .... getting to school on time.

3 Adrian is .... French.

4 Adrian is .... English.

5 Adrian is .... handwriting.

6 Adrian is .... art.

7 Adrian is .... maths.

8 Adrian is .... music.

Shapes
Who is hiding behind the wall?
Can you fit the shapes into the wall and write the letters in the correct places?
Then read the description and find the boy who is hiding.

Equations

Find the correct verbs from the box to fill the gaps in the sentences. Write the numbers of the verbs to find the *x* and *y* coordinates of two points on each grid. Draw the points on the grids. Join the points on each grid to make a graph. Find the correct equation for each graph. The first one has been done for you.

3 am watching
6 watched
4 am going to go
5 went
1 bought
2 am going to buy
-4 am going to play
-1 played
0 am doing
3 did
-2 am going to take
-3 am taking

Equations
$y = x + 1$
$y = x - 3$
$y = 2x$

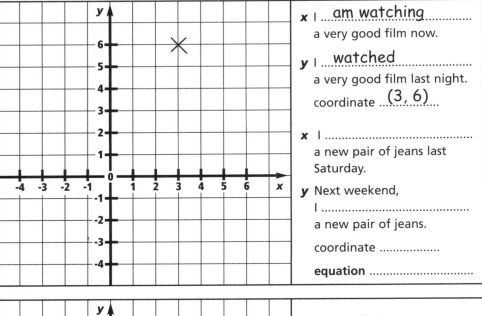

x I ..am watching.......... a very good film now.

y I ..watched.......... a very good film last night.

coordinate ...(3, 6)....

x I .... a new pair of jeans last Saturday.

y Next weekend, I .... a new pair of jeans.

coordinate ....

equation ....

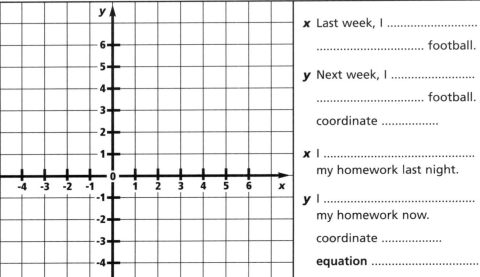

x Last week, I .... football.

y Next week, I .... football.

coordinate ....

x I .... my homework last night.

y I .... my homework now.

coordinate ....

equation ....

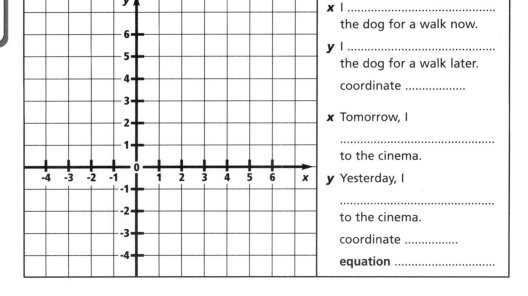

x I .... the dog for a walk now.

y I .... the dog for a walk later.

coordinate ....

x Tomorrow, I .... to the cinema.

y Yesterday, I .... to the cinema.

coordinate ....

equation ....

Decimals

A group of friends are showing each other photos
and talking about what they used to do when they were little.
Do the decimal calculations and choose the correct answers. Find out whether each sentence
is *true* or *false*. Write the name of the correct person under each photo.

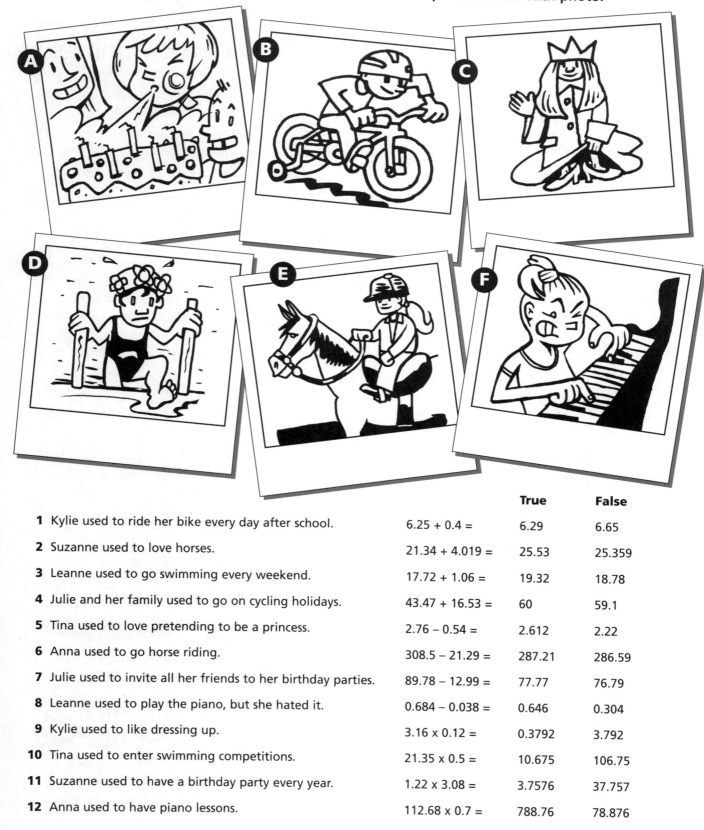

		True	False
1 Kylie used to ride her bike every day after school.	6.25 + 0.4 =	6.29	6.65
2 Suzanne used to love horses.	21.34 + 4.019 =	25.53	25.359
3 Leanne used to go swimming every weekend.	17.72 + 1.06 =	19.32	18.78
4 Julie and her family used to go on cycling holidays.	43.47 + 16.53 =	60	59.1
5 Tina used to love pretending to be a princess.	2.76 – 0.54 =	2.612	2.22
6 Anna used to go horse riding.	308.5 – 21.29 =	287.21	286.59
7 Julie used to invite all her friends to her birthday parties.	89.78 – 12.99 =	77.77	76.79
8 Leanne used to play the piano, but she hated it.	0.684 – 0.038 =	0.646	0.304
9 Kylie used to like dressing up.	3.16 x 0.12 =	0.3792	3.792
10 Tina used to enter swimming competitions.	21.35 x 0.5 =	10.675	106.75
11 Suzanne used to have a birthday party every year.	1.22 x 3.08 =	3.7576	37.757
12 Anna used to have piano lessons.	112.68 x 0.7 =	788.76	78.876

Theme Park Arithmetic

**Fun World is the biggest theme park in the world. Can you spot all the maths mistakes?
Correct the maths and complete the sentences in the box.**

WATERFALL

Two adults and three children, please.

That's £15, please

£2.50

JOB OPPORTUNITIES
Are you aged 18 or over?

We always have job opportunities at **Fun World**.

We have 48 rides and we need to employ 3 people on each ride.

We have a total of 126 employees.

FUN WORLD FOOD
Hot dogs	**£1.50**
Hamburgers	**£2**
Coke	**£1.20**

That's £4.70, please.

I'd like a hamburger, a hot dog and two cokes, please.

DARTS

10
50
25

Prizes
150 points: giant teddy
100 points: small teddy
50 points: key ring

You win a key ring.

Adults **£10**
Children **£7**

Today only: 50% off all entrance fees

One adult and four children, please.

That's £13, please.

FUN WORLD VISITORS

1 million people visit Fun World every week.

That's 63 visitors every year!

Theme Park Arithmetic

BIGGEST ROLLERCOASTER IN THE WORLD

Speed: 120 kilometres per hour
Track: 6 kilometres long
Time: The ride lasts 5 minutes

LOTTERY

Add up the numbers on your tickets.
These totals win prizes.

5000   wins £2
7500   wins £3
10,000   wins £10
15,000   wins £50

You win £2.

1272
3183
5545

SOUVENIR SHOP

I've been to Fun World
£15

£12

FW £4

FWO

I'd like a T-shirt, a mug and a baseball cap.

free with two or more items

The baseball cap is £5, sir.

ENTRANCE

It should cost ....

VISITORS

There should be .... visitors every year.

JOB OPPORTUNITIES

Fun World should have a total of .... employees.

DARTS

The girl should win a ....

WATERFALL

It should cost ....

FUN WORLD FOOD

It should cost..................... .

BIGGEST ROLLERCOASTER IN THE WORLD

The ride should last .... minutes.

LOTTERY

The boy should win ....

SOUVENIR SHOP

The .... should be free.

Word Calculations

Use your arithmetic skills to make compound adjectives.
Each letter has a different value.
Add up the letters in each word to find the second part of each compound adjective.

The first one has been done for you as an example.

A = 1	N = 14
B = 2	O = 15
C = 3	P = 16
D = 4	Q = 17
E = 5	R = 18
F = 6	S = 19
G = 7	T = 20
H = 8	U = 21
I = 9	V = 22
J = 10	W = 23
K = 11	X = 24
L = 12	Y = 25
M = 13	Z = 26

big-headed
b + i + g = 2 + 9 + 7 = 18

long- ....

hard ....

kind- ....

back- ....

tight- ....

computer- ....

quick- ....

bad- ....

home ....

7	tempered
17	breaking
~~18~~	~~headed~~
31	working
38	hearted
41	made
48	winded
61	witted
64	fisted
111	literate

Now find the definition for each compound adjective and complete the sentences.
Don't worry if you can't find them all.
Just multiply the first letter of each part of the adjective together.
For example, **back-breaking**: b x b = 2 x 2 = 4

4 Work that is very hard and tiring is ..... *back-breaking* ..... .

16 Someone who thinks that they are very clever and important is ....

36 Someone who knows how to use a computer is ....

40 Someone who is often angry is ....

88 Someone who is sympathetic to other people is ....

104 Something that you have made yourself is ....

120 Someone who doesn't like to spend or give away their money is ....

184 Someone who is always busy is ....

276 A speech or a book that is much too long is ....

391 Someone who is very intelligent is ....

Sleep

We all need to sleep every day.
The chart shows how many hours sleep you need at different times in your life.
Read the sentences about how much sleep these people need.
Can you choose the correct age for each person? You don't need to use all the ages in the box.

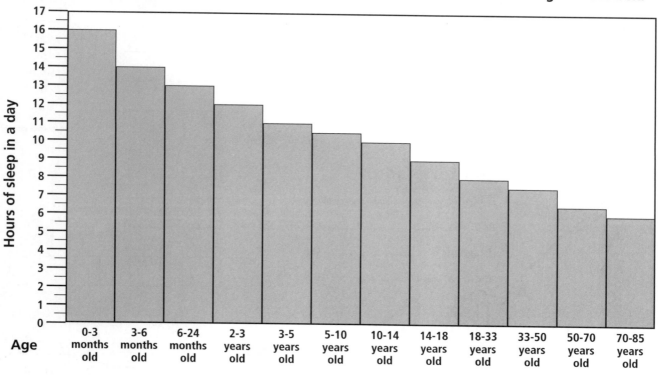

Hours of sleep in a day (y-axis, 0 to 17)

Age (x-axis): 0-3 months old, 3-6 months old, 6-24 months old, 2-3 years old, 3-5 years old, 5-10 years old, 10-14 years old, 14-18 years old, 18-33 years old, 33-50 years old, 50-70 years old, 70-85 years old

1 Moira needs eight hours sleep every night.
How old is she? ...twenty-eight years old...

2 Jason needs twelve hours sleep every night.
How old is he? ....

3 Daniel only needs six and a half hours sleep every night.
How old is he? ....

4 Hilary needs to sleep for fourteen hours every day.
How old is she? ....

5 Natasha needs to sleep for nine hours every night.
How old is she? ....

6 Russell needs ten and a half hours sleep every night.
How old is he? ....

7 James needs sixteen hours sleep every day.
How old is he? ....

8 Rachel needs to sleep for seven and a half hours every night.
How old is she? ....

eighteen years old
five months old
seventy-nine years old
two months old
sixty-one years old
two and a half years old
four years old
thirteen years old
sixteen months old
forty-three years old
seven and a half years old
~~twenty-eight years old~~

Do you get enough sleep?

How old are you? ....

How much sleep do you need? ....

What time do you go to bed? ....

What time do you get up? ....

How much sleep do you get every night?

....

Dinosaurs

Complete the descriptions of the four dinosaurs. Choose four words in each box
and write them in the crosswords. Then write the words in the sentences.
There is one extra word in each box.

❶ Compsognathus

It is a (a) .... runner

and it is (b) ....

It has (c) .... legs

and a (d) .... tail.

fast
thin
small
fat
long

❷ Pteranadon

It has (a) .... wings

and very (b) .... arms.

It has a (c) .... tail

and a (d) .... beak.

small
enormous
long
thin
short

❸ Diplodocus

It is (a) .... and (b) ....

It has a (c) .... head and

a very (d) .... neck.

long
short
huge
small
heavy

Dinosaurs

4 Tyrannosaurus rex

It is very (a) .... and (b) .... ,

but it has (c) .... arms.

It has (d) .... teeth.

```
          a
      c   ┌───┐
 b → ┌───┬───┼───┬───┬───┐
     └───┴───┴───┴───┴───┘
     c↓
   d ┌───┬───┬───┬───┐
     └───┼───┴───┴───┘
         └───┐
         │   │
         └───┘
```

strong
big
long
sharp
small

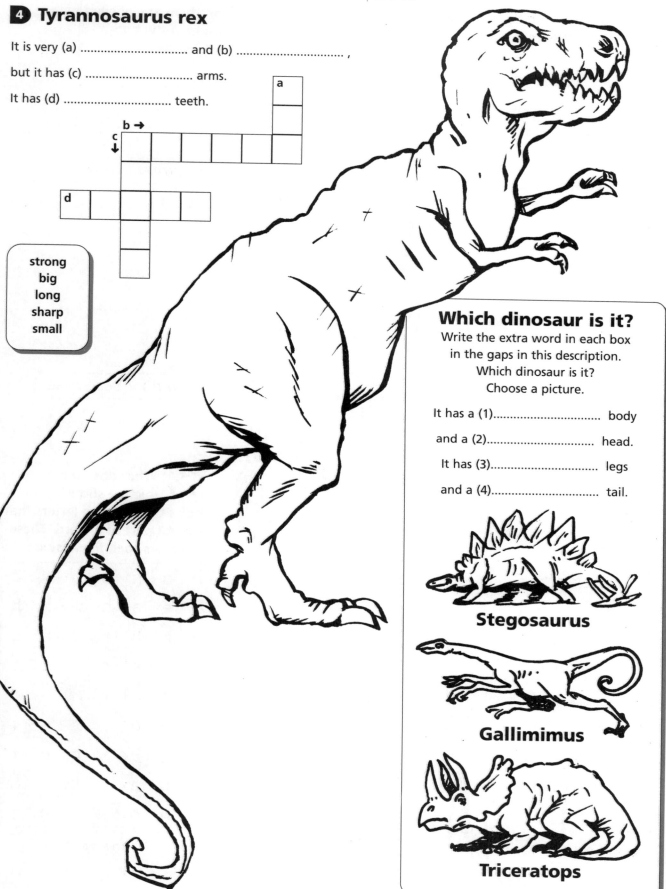

Which dinosaur is it?

Write the extra word in each box in the gaps in this description. Which dinosaur is it? Choose a picture.

It has a (1)............................ body

and a (2)............................ head.

It has (3)............................ legs

and a (4)............................ tail.

Stegosaurus

Gallimimus

Triceratops

Bones

All the bones in the human body have scientific names. Some of them are labelled here.
Where is each bone in the body? Find the words for parts of the body
in the wordsearch and write them in the correct places.

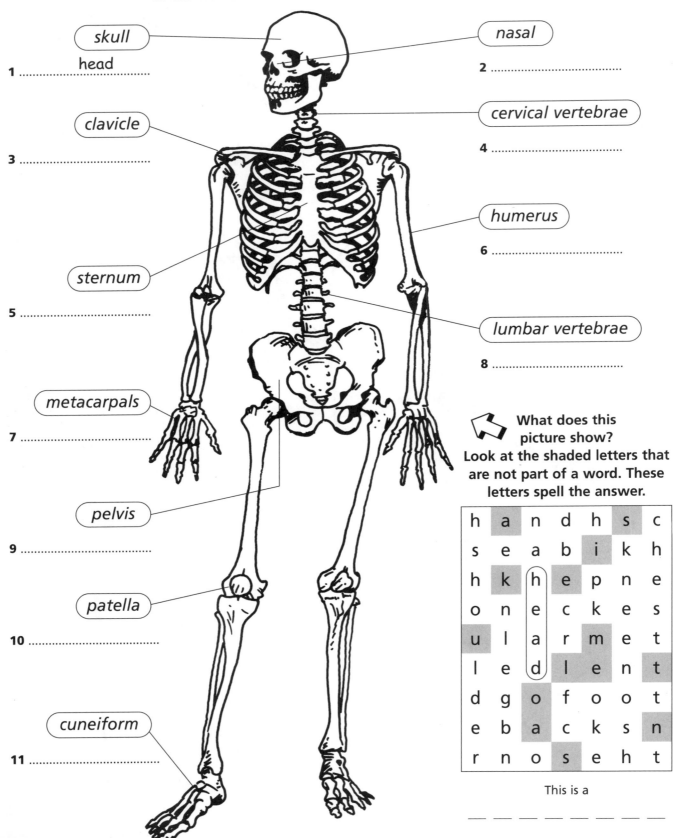

skull
head
1 ....

nasal
2 ....

clavicle
3 ....

cervical vertebrae
4 ....

sternum
5 ....

humerus
6 ....

lumbar vertebrae
8 ....

metacarpals
7 ....

pelvis
9 ....

patella
10 ....

cuneiform
11 ....

What does this picture show?
Look at the shaded letters that
are not part of a word. These
letters spell the answer.

h	a	n	d	h	s	c
s	e	a	b	i	k	h
h	k	h	e	p	n	e
o	n	e	c	k	e	s
u	l	a	r	m	e	t
l	e	d	l	e	n	t
d	g	o	f	o	o	t
e	b	a	c	k	s	n
r	n	o	s	e	h	t

This is a

_ _ _ _ _ _ _ _ _

The Solar System

There are nine planets in the Solar System.

Complete the questions with the name of the correct planet. Then write the answers.

> **a** 150 million km *Earth*   **d** 142,984 km in diameter *Jupiter*
>
> **b** 462°C *Venus*   **e** −235°C *Pluto*
>
> **c** 18 *Saturn*   **f** 172,248 km/h *Mercury*

1 How fast does ....Mercury........... travel?

.....172,248 km/h.....

2 How far away from the Sun is .... ?

....

3 How big is .... ?

....

4 How many moons has .... got?

....

5 How cold is .... ?

....

6 How hot is .... ?

....

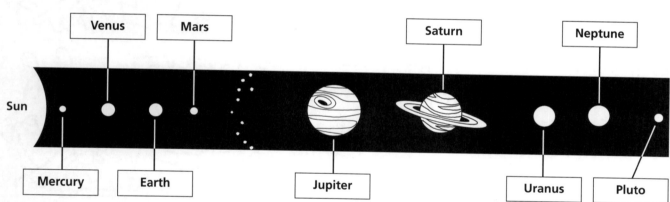

Sun

Venus   Mars   Saturn   Neptune

Mercury   Earth   Jupiter   Uranus   Pluto

Write the names of the planets next to the corresponding numbers in the grid and find the name of the biggest comet in the Solar System.

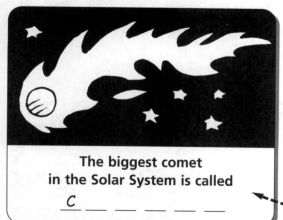

The biggest comet in the Solar System is called

C _ _ _ _ _ _

1	M	E	R	C	U	R	Y
2							
3							
4							
5							
6							

Technology

Modern technology makes our lives easier and helps us to learn more about the world and the universe. Here are some of the things that we have because of technology.

Can you find the correct sentence to describe each thing?

1 camcorder

You can play a tune on a camcorder. (**S**)

You can do your maths homework with a camcorder. (**L**)

You can film your friends and family with a camcorder. (**M**)

2 mouse

You can choose television programmes with a mouse. (**A**)

You can take a photograph with a mouse. (**O**)

You can control your computer with a mouse. (**I**)

3 microwave

You can cook your dinner in a microwave. (**C**)

You can listen to music with a microwave. (**V**)

You can see very small objects with a microwave. (**T**)

4 shower

You can have a wash in a shower. (**R**)

You can watch a film at the shower. (**H**)

You can look at the stars with a shower. (**B**)

5 vacuum cleaner

You can clean your carpets with a vacuum cleaner. (**O**)

You can boil water in a vacuum cleaner. (**U**)

You can wash your clothes in a vacuum cleaner. (**E**)

Technology

6 credit card

You can tell the time
with a credit card. (**G**)

You can buy things
with a credit card. (**C**)

You can drive to school
in a credit card. (**N**)

7 space shuttle

You can travel to Mars
in a space shuttle. (**H**)

You can play games on
a space shuttle. (**R**)

You can dry your hair
with a space shuttle. (**J**)

8 fridge

You can cut your grass
with a fridge. (**A**)

You can make clothes
with a fridge. (**E**)

You can keep food cold
in a fridge. (**I**)

9 mobile phone

You can fly to Australia
in a mobile phone. (**D**)

You can go for a ride
on a mobile phone. (**F**)

You can talk to your friends
on a mobile phone. (**P**)

**Write the letters next to the answers
you choose and find the name of something
that is very important in modern technology.**

_ _ _ _ _ _

Memory

How good is your memory? Look at the pictures for two minutes.
Then cover the pictures and write all the words you can remember.

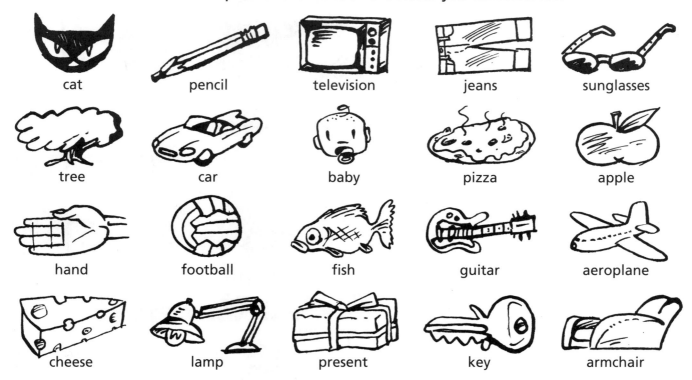

cat	pencil	television	jeans	sunglasses
tree	car	baby	pizza	apple
hand	football	fish	guitar	aeroplane
cheese	lamp	present	key	armchair

How many things did you remember?

Now look at these pictures for two minutes. This time, make up a story about all the things.
Then cover the pictures and write all the words you can remember.

bicycle	towel	rucksack	mug	book
candle	watch	flowers	banana	sandwich
rabbit	computer	bread	table	ring
telephone	trainers	bird	soap	T-shirt

Did you remember more things this time?

Senses

We have five senses: sight, hearing, touch, taste and smell.

Can you find your way through the maze? Make sentences to describe what the things in the pictures *look*, *sound*, *feel*, *taste* and *smell* like. You can only move to a circle that is next to the one you are on. You must use every word once and you must describe the pictures in the correct order. Write the numbers of the pictures in the circles, at the beginning of the sentences.

1 a cake

2 a jumper

3 a skunk

4 a baby

5 the drums

6 a rose

7 a brick

8 an olive

9 a needle

10 a cat

11 a lemon

12 a bin

13 a book

14 a picture of flowers

15 a mouse

16 some crisps

17 a dog

The pH Scale

The pH scale tells us how **acidic** and **alkaline** different substances are.
We test the substances with an **indicator** and the indicator changes colour.
This chart shows the pH scale and some substances with different pH numbers.

Can you solve the anagrams and find out the colour of the indicator for each pH number?
Colour the sections of the chart.

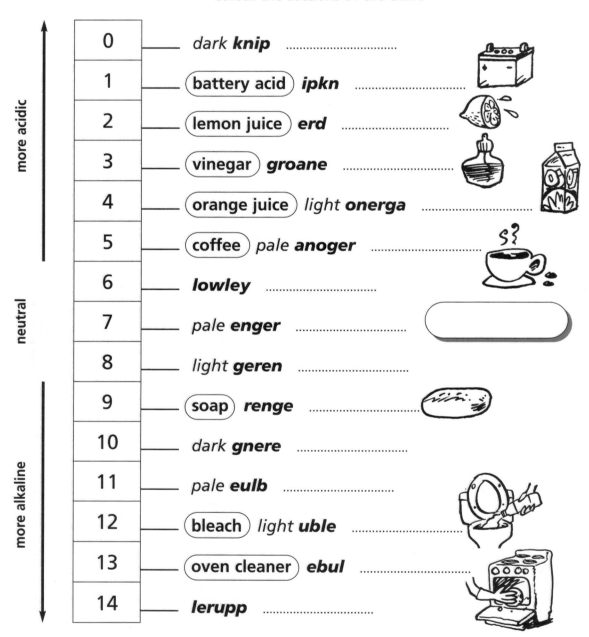

	0	dark **knip** ....
more acidic	1	(battery acid) **ipkn** ....
	2	(lemon juice) **erd** ....
	3	(vinegar) **groane** ....
	4	(orange juice) light **onerga** ....
	5	(coffee) pale **anoger** ....
neutral	6	**lowley** ....
	7	pale **enger** ....
	8	light **geren** ....
more alkaline	9	(soap) **renge** ....
	10	dark **gnere** ....
	11	pale **eulb** ....
	12	(bleach) light **uble** ....
	13	(oven cleaner) **ebul** ....
	14	**lerupp** ....

Substances with a pH number of 7 are neutral. That means that they are not acidic or alkaline. Choose the correct word to complete each sentence. Write the letters to find a substance that is neutral. Write it next to number 7 on the chart.

a Bleach is (w) **more** / (g) **less** alkaline than soap.

b Orange juice is (a) **more** / (i) **less** acidic than coffee.

c Vinegar is (s) **more** / (t) **less** acidic than battery acid.

d Soap is (o) **more** / (e) **less** alkaline than oven cleaner.

e Orange juice is (y) **more** / (r) **less** acidic than vinegar.

Food Web

A food web shows which food animals eat. The arrows are missing from this food web.
Choose the correct answer to each question. The correct answers are also grammatically correct.
Then draw the arrows on the food web.

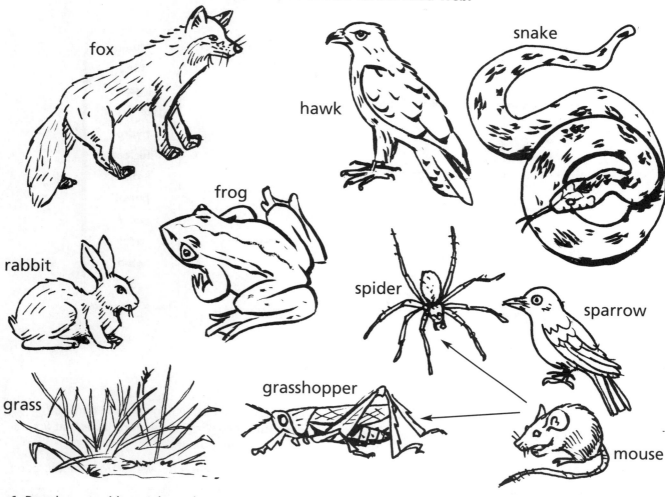

1 Do mice eat spiders and grasshoppers?	*Yes, they do.* ✔	*No, they aren't.*
2 Is a snake a good meal for a rabbit?	*Yes, it has.*	*No, it isn't.*
3 Are snakes good at catching sparrows and hawks?	*Yes, they can.*	*No, they aren't.*
4 Can spiders eat grasshoppers?	*Yes, they can.*	*No, they haven't.*
5 Are rabbits and mice good food for foxes?	*Yes, they are.*	*No, they can't.*
6 Have rabbits got strong teeth for eating snakes and sparrows?	*Yes, they are.*	*No, they haven't.*
7 Can snakes eat spiders, frogs and mice?	*Yes, they can.*	*No, they aren't.*
8 Are grasshoppers and spiders good food for sparrows?	*Yes, they are.*	*No, they can't.*
9 Do frogs eat grass?	*Yes, they have.*	*No, they don't.*
10 Can frogs catch spiders?	*Yes, they can.*	*No, they don't.*
11 Have hawks got strong beaks for eating rabbits, snakes and sparrows?	*Yes, they have.*	*No, they don't.*
12 Do foxes eat frogs?	*Yes, they do.*	*No, they aren't.*
13 Can mice eat snakes and sparrows?	*Yes, they do.*	*No, they can't.*
14 Do grasshoppers, mice and rabbits like eating grass?	*Yes, they do.*	*No, they haven't.*
15 Are frogs good at catching grasshoppers?	*Yes, they are.*	*No, they can't.*

Energy Crossword

This crossword is all about different kinds of energy.
Use the words from the box to complete the crossword

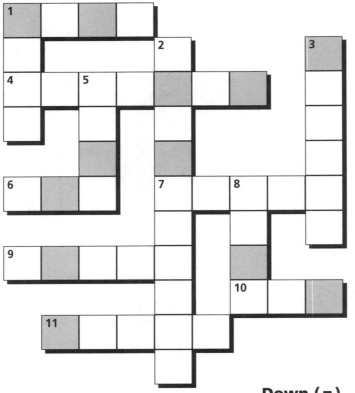

| coal |
| dung |
| gas |
| geothermal |
| hydro |
| nuclear |
| oil |
| petrol |
| solar |
| tidal |
| wind |
| wood |

Across (↓)

1 .... comes from trees. About half the people in the world burn it for heating and cooking.

4 .... energy comes from uranium. Many people think that it is too dangerous.

6 .... is a liquid. It comes from under the ground.

7 .... electric energy comes from powerful waterfalls that fall from lakes.

9 .... energy comes from the sun. It is often used to power calculators.

10 .... comes from under the ground. Some cookers use it instead of electricity.

11 .... energy comes from the sea. When the tide goes in and out the energy is made into electricity.

Down (↓)

1 .... energy is used to make electricity. It comes from giant turbines that are usually on the top of hills.

2 In Iceland, people use hot water from underground to heat their houses. It is called .... energy.

3 .... is made from oil. We use it in our cars.

5 .... is black and it comes from underground. We get it from mines.

8 In some countries people make gas from cow ....

This picture shows the place where electricity is made. Can you rearrange the letters in the shaded squares to find out what it is called?

_ _ _ _ _

_ _ _ _ _ _ _ _ _

The Human Body

These sentences describe what eight parts of the body do, but lots of the words are missing.
Can you find the words in the box and fill in the gaps?
You need to find 10 nouns (n) and 6 verbs (v).

1 The (n) *bra...*
(v) *cont...*
the body.

2 The lungs
(v) *tak...*
oxygen from the
(n) *air* .

3 The (n) *hear...*
pumps
(n) *blood*
around the body.

4 The stomach
(v) *digest...*
food.

5 The (n) *ski...*
(v) *protec...*
the body from damage and
(n) *disea...* .

air	filter
blood	food
brain	heart
carry	information
cells	kidneys
controls	protects
digests	skin
disease	take

6 The (n) *kidny...*
(v) *filte...*
waste products from blood.

7 Nerves
(v) *carr...*
(n) *inf...*
to and from the brain.

8 Blood carries oxygen and
(n) *food*
to the
(n) *cell,* .

Predicting the Future

Which of these things do you think will happen in the future?
Write *will*, *won't* or *might* in the gap in each sentence.

If you choose *will*, complete the end of the sentence. Write when you think this thing will happen.
If you choose *won't* or *might*, cross out the end of the sentence.

For example:

Scientists ...**will**... discover a cure for AIDS in ...**twenty**... years' time.

People ...**won't**... travel to distant galaxies ~~in .... years' time.~~

1 We .... have robots to do all our housework in .... years' time.

2 People .... live in space cities in .... years' time.

3 We .... have flying cars and motorbikes in .... years' time.

4 Scientists .... discover a cure for AIDS in .... years' time.

5 We .... have watches that are telephones and give us Internet access in .... years' time.

6 Scientists .... develop robots that are more intelligent than people in .... years' time.

7 People .... travel to distant galaxies in .... years' time.

8 We .... get all our energy from renewable sources, such as the wind and sun, in .... years' time.

9 We .... communicate with intelligent life forms on other planets in .... years' time.

10 People .... have a 'smart' card that says everything about them – passport, driving licence, medical details, qualifications, etc. in .... years' time.

Write your own predictions for the future here.

....

....

....

....

Animal Groups

Many animals live together in groups. Read about life in a pack of wolves.
Choose the correct ending for each sentence and write the correct number in the box.
Write the underlined words in the wheel next to the correct number.
Unscramble the shaded letters in the wheel to spell the word
for how animals act with each other.

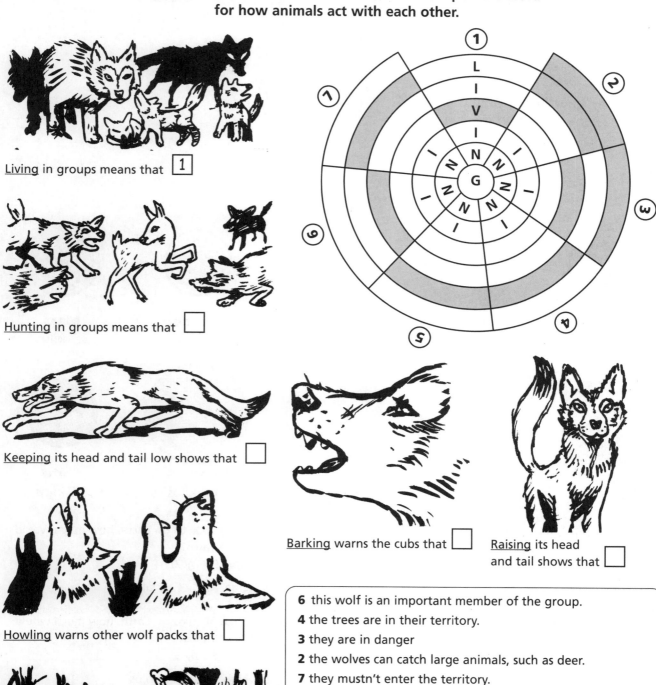

Living in groups means that ☐ 1

Hunting in groups means that ☐

Keeping its head and tail low shows that ☐

Barking warns the cubs that ☐

Raising its head and tail shows that ☐

Howling warns other wolf packs that ☐

6 this wolf is an important member of the group.

4 the trees are in their territory.

3 they are in danger

2 the wolves can catch large animals, such as deer.

7 they mustn't enter the territory.

5 this is an inferior wolf in the group.

1 the wolves can protect each other and teach the cubs.

Marking trees with
scent tells other wolves that ☐

How animals act when they are together
is called **animal**

☐ ☐ ☐ ☐ ☐ ☐ ☐ ☐ ☐

Weight

You probably know how much you weigh on Earth. But would you weigh the same if you went to the other planets in the Solar System? The answer is no because the force of gravity on each planet is different. If you went to Jupiter you would weigh a lot more than on Earth, and if you went to Pluto you would weigh a lot less.

Here are the equivalent weights for 10 kilos on Earth on all the planets in the Solar System.

Answer the questions to find out the equivalent weight on the sun.

the sun

.... kilos

Mercury
3.7 kilos

Venus
9 kilos

Earth
10 kilos

the moon
1.6 kilos

Mars
3.7 kilos

Jupiter
23.6 kilos

Saturn
9.1 kilos

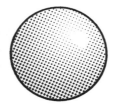

Uranus
8.8 kilos

Neptune
11.2 kilos

Pluto
0.6 kilos

1 If you weighed 60 kilos on Earth, how much would you weigh on Mercury?
(Clue: multiply 3.7 by 6)

I would weigh .... kilos.

2 If you weighed 40 kilos on Earth, how much would you weigh on Jupiter?
(Clue: multiply 23.6 by 4)

I would weigh .... kilos.

3 If you weighed 50 kilos on Earth, how much would you weigh on Neptune?
(Clue: multiply 11.2 by 5)

I would weigh .... kilos.

4 If you weighed 70 kilos on Earth, how much would you weigh on Saturn?
(Clue: multiply 9.1 by 7)

I would weigh .... kilos.

5 If you weighed 30 kilos on Earth, how much would you weigh on Uranus?
(Clue: multiply 8.8 by 3)

I would weigh .... kilos.

6 If you weighed 50 kilos on Earth, how much would you weigh on the moon?
(Clue: multiply 1.6 by 5)

I would weigh .... kilos.

To find the equivalent weight on the sun for 10 kilos on Earth, add all your answers together.

Who Are You?

Draw your face in the middle of the page.
Complete the speech bubbles with information about yourself.

I come from
....

My name is
....

My telephone number is
....

I am ....
years old.

My address is
....
....
....

I live in
....

I've got
.... sisters
and
.... brothers.

I've got .... pet(s).
Its/Their name(s) is/are
....
....

My mum is a
....
and my dad is a
....

I'm good at
....

I'm bad at
....

My favourite food is
....

My favourite sport is
....

My favourite place is
....

My favourite computer game is
....

My favourite group/singer is
....

My favourite subject at school is
....

My friends are called
....

I love
....

I hate
....

Fruit and Vegetables

Match up the parts of words to find ten fruits and vegetables. Label the pictures.

ca	ba	pe	b	pot	or	~~gr~~	to	str	swe
rr	~~ap~~	an	awbe	ea	etc	na	pp	ma	at
orn	oes	~~es~~	ge	ots	er	rry	ns	to	na

1 grapes

2 ....

3 ....

4 ....

5 ....

6 ....

7 ....

8 ....

9 ....

10 ....

Keep a fruit and vegetables diary for one week.
Write all the fruit and vegetables you eat at each meal.

Monday	**Tuesday**	**Wednesday**
Breakfast	Breakfast	Breakfast ....
Lunch	Lunch	Lunch ....
Dinner	Dinner	Dinner ....
Snacks	Snacks	Snacks ....

Thursday	**Friday**	**Saturday**
Breakfast	Breakfast	Breakfast ....
Lunch	Lunch	Lunch ....
Dinner	Dinner	Dinner ....
Snacks	Snacks	Snacks ....

Sunday

Breakfast ....

Lunch   ....

Dinner   ....

Snacks   ....

Do you eat enough fruit and vegetables? You need to eat five portions every day. How many portions do you eat every day?

Monday ....   Tuesday ....   Wednesday ....

Thursday ....   Friday ....   Saturday ....

Sunday ....

Girls and Boys

Are girls and boys different?
Look at the adjectives and decide if each one describes girls or boys better.
Write the *correct form* of the adjective in the box you think it belongs in.

For example:
Girls are **cheekier** than boys.

cheeky	silly	kind	funny	lazy	rough	bossy	polite	brave
clever	shy	friendly	quiet	sporty	tidy	rude		

Boys are ...

than girls.

Girls are ...

than boys.

Now think of two friends and write their names.

a male friend .... a female friend ....

What are your friends like? Complete two new boxes to describe your friends.
Choose adjectives from the list above.

.... **is ...**

than .... **.**

.... **is ...**

than .... **.**

Which Job?

You need to study different subjects to do different jobs.
Look at these jobs and decide which school subjects you need to study to do each job.

1 computer programmer — f

2 athlete — d

3 accountant — i

4 actor — m

5 doctor — b

6 air steward — l

7 chef — a

8 carpenter — o

9 journalist — j

10 museum guide — e

11 company director — g

12 painter — h

13 astronomer — k

14 pop star — n

15 fashion designer — c

a cookery	**f** information technology	**k** physics
b biology and chemistry	**g** business studies	**l** languages
c textiles	**h** art	**m** drama
d sports	**i** maths	**n** music
e history	**j** English	**o** woodwork

Which Job?

Mystery Job

Now use the answers to draw the mystery object.
Copy each square exactly in the correct place on the grid.

What is it?

Which person uses it?

a a teacher

b a hairdresser

c a nurse

d a farmer

e a cleaner

1	2	3
4	5	6
7	8	9
10	11	12
13	14	15

a
b
c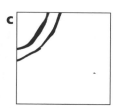
d
e

f
g
h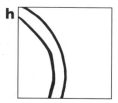
i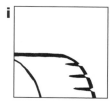
j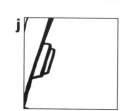

k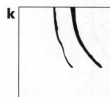
l
m
n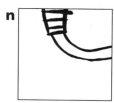
o

A Healthy Life

Here are fifteen tips for a healthy life. Choose the correct word to complete each tip.

1 Eat lots of ....

2 Don't ....

3 Sleep for .... hours every night.

4 Eat .... every day.

5 Drink lots of .... when you are exercising.

6 Play lots of ....

7 Take the .... in the shopping centre.

8 .... to school.

9 Have a .... after sports.

10 Exercise for about .... every day.

11 Don't take ....

12 Drink .... at breakfast time.

13 Exercise .... as often as you can.

14 Go running ....

15 Don't stay .... too long.

meat • *fruit and vegetables*

exercise • *smoke*

nine • *five*

breakfast • *sweets*

water • *Coca Cola*

computer games • *sports*

stairs • *lift*

Travel by bus or car • *Walk or cycle*

shower • *hamburger*

one hour • *seven hours*

holidays • *drugs*

coffee • *milk*

inside • *outside*

in the park • *in the street*

in the sun • *at school*

Ask your teacher for the answers, then find your medal. Colour your medal.

1–5 points

6–10 points

11–15 points

Saving Money

**Are you good with money? Think of something big that you would like.
For example, some expensive jeans, a holiday or a CD player.
This plan will help you to save the money you need.**

What would you like to buy? (A) ....

How much does it cost? (B) ....

How much money do you have already? (C) ....

How much more money do you need? (D) .... (B – C)
(This is how much money
you need to save.)

How much money do you get every week?

pocket money: ....

jobs: ....

TOTAL: (E) ....

How much do you spend every week?

snacks: ....

going out: ....

clothes: ....

magazines: ....

other things: ....

TOTAL: (F) ....

How much can you save every week? (G) .... (E – F)

How many weeks do you need to save the money you need?

(H).. (D ÷ G)

Is this too long to wait?

How can you save more money?
Write three ideas here. For example: *I'm not going to buy magazines.*
I'm going to take snacks from home to school every day.

1 ....

2 ....

3 ....

How Do You Feel?

Can you find the words to describe how these people are feeling?
There are lots of words that you don't need.

s u n n y h u n g r y s m a l l f r e e o l d f a t p o l i t e l o n e l y

Left margin (top to bottom): c o l d t i r e d n e r v o u s u p s e t l a r g e t h i n w a r m h a r d q u i c k a n g r y s c a r e d

Right margin (bottom to top): s o f t s h i n y a n n o y e d n e w g r e e d y t i n y e x c i t e d s a d k i n d y o u n g

1 I've got an exam tomorrow.
I feel _ **e** _ _ _ _ **u** _ .

2 All my friends have gone on holiday. I feel **l** _ _ _ _ _ _ .

3 My mum and dad are getting a divorce. I feel _ **a** _ .

4 My best friend has a new friend. I feel **u** _ _ _ _ _ .

5 I've walked 20 kilometres today. I feel _ **i** _ **e** _ .

6 Today is the start of the summer holidays.
I feel _ **r** _ _ .

7 I've missed the bus.
I feel _ **n** _ _ **y** _ _ .

8 I got an A in my English exam. I feel _ **a** _ _ **y** _ .

9 My friend has stolen my watch. I feel _ _ _ **g** _ _ _ .

10 It's my first day at a new school. I feel _ **c** _ _ **e** _ .

11 I haven't eaten anything since breakfast.
I feel _ **u** _ _ _ _ .

12 I'm going on holiday.
I feel _ _ **c** _ **t** _ _ _ .

Bottom margin: l o n g l a z y p r e t t y h a p p y s h o r t e n o r m o u s s m o o t h

Summer Plans

The summer holidays are fun – good weather and no school. But they can be boring, too. What are you going to do this summer? Make your plans for a more exciting summer.

Learn a new sport

Choose three sports that you've never done but that you would like to try.
Here are some ideas, but you can think of your own ideas, too.

I'd like to try ...

....

....

....

surfing   tennis   hang-gliding   sailing

scuba diving   windsurfing   go-karting

rock climbing   ice skating   rollerblading

canoeing   judo   basketball

Work for a charity

Choose three groups you would like to help.

I'd like to help ...

....

....

....

homeless people   disabled children

people in the Third World   young children

children with learning difficulties   animals

children in hospital   elderly people

Try something new

Choose three things that you have never done before but would like to try.
Here are some ideas, but you can think of your own ideas, too.

I'd like to...

....

....

....

organise a party for my friends   act in a play

cook dinner for my family   write a song

learn to do magic tricks   learn a musical instrument

organise a day out with my friends   make something

Ask your teachers or look in the phone book and on the Internet to find out how to do these things.

Ask a teacher or youth group leader about how to contact charities.

Ask your sports teacher or your local sports centre for information on where you can learn new sports.

Now choose **three** activities that you are **definitely** going to do this summer.

I am going to ...   .

....

....

How are you going to organise these activities?

....

....

....

....

Making Conversation

Going to a party can sometimes be difficult if you don't know many people there.
It can be hard to start talking to people. Here are nine tips for having a good conversation.
Can you find the heading for each tip? Write the headings in the boxes above the tips.

a Use body language
b Listen
c Say goodbye
d Tell a joke
e Find common interests
f Don't be shy
g Introduce yourself
h Give details
i Be prepared

1 Before you go to the party, think of topics to talk about. For example, a film you've seen, something that happened at school or a CD you like. This will make talking a lot easier.

2 Be the first to say hello. If someone looks interesting, talk to them!

3 Say your name and ask for the other person's name.

4 Smile and look into the person's eyes. Don't fold your arms.

5 Ask the person about their favourite music, hobbies and school subjects so you can find things you are both interested in.

6 Show interest in what the other person says. Answer their questions. Ask them questions about the things they like to do.

7 When the other person asks you questions, give full answers. Don't just say 'yes' or 'no'.

8 Think of a funny thing that has happened to you. Tell this funny story to your new friend.

9 Don't just disappear at the end of the conversation. Say you've enjoyed talking to the person and say goodbye.

When you've finished the activity, colour the correct numbers and letters in the square. Find a word that is useful for starting a conversation!

7a	5f	4h	8a		9g	7f	9f	1e
8g		3a	2d	2b	3c		5c	
	9d	2g	5d		1h	1	4b	
		6c	4c		4a		8f	
1e	5e	4e		6h	7c	5i	8h	
3b	2f	1i		8d	3h			
4d	7h	9i	3g	6g	9c	9f	2e	
1f	6b				9c		6a	8c
3i	7e	8i		5g			7g	

Babysitting

This babysitter isn't doing a very good job. Can you tell her what is wrong?
There are at least twelve mistakes in the picture. Write sentences using *should/shouldn't*.

1 ....

2 ....

3 ....

4 ....

5 ....

6 ....

7 ....

8 ....

9 ....

10 ....

11 ....

12 ....

Summer Jobs

Find thirteen places where teenagers can find jobs in the summer.

Start with the letter *r* in the top right-hand corner. You can move up (↑) and down (↓), right (→) and left (←), but not diagonally. Some of the places are one word and some are two words. Each new word starts in a black square.

Write the names of the places.

Example:

restaurant
....

r	t	f	a	r	m	r	k	e	t
e	n	t	o	l	c	a	n	u	f
s	a	h	n	t	r	m	f	a	i
t	r	e	e	s	e	t	e	p	r
a	u	s	g	u	p	s	h	r	k
o	h	s	a	p	s	p	o	a	e
p	h	o	s	o	b	g	p	m	t
o	e	t	w	r	u	i	o	m	m
f	c	e	e	t	l	f	h	u	u
f	i	l	n	s	c	t	s	e	s

1 ....

2 ....

3 ....

4 ....

5 ....

6 ....

Summer Jobs

7 ....

8 ....

9 ....

10 ....

11 ....

12 ....

Which job?
Read about each person's personality, interests and ambitions.
Where should each person have a summer job?

a Deborah is very fashionable and she likes looking good. She would like to study to be a fashion designer when she leaves school.

....

b Curtis is very good at history. He is quite shy and he likes being quiet. He would like to study archaeology at university.

....

c Samir is adventurous and he is always making jokes and laughing. He loves taking risks. He wants to be a racing car driver when he grows up.

....

d Pedro enjoys working on the computer. He is quiet and helpful. He wants to be a secretary when he finishes college.

....

e Maria loves playing volleyball and badminton. She also likes swimming and athletics. She wants to be an aerobics instructor when she is 18.

....

f Bianca loves animals. She is confident and she enjoys meeting people. She would like to be a businesswoman when she is older.

....

Where would you like to have a summer job? Why?

Bullying

Bullying is a big problem in schools. Have you ever bullied someone?

Look at the pictures and choose the correct verb to complete each sentence.
Tick the sentences that are true for you. Then think about why you did it. Will you do it again?

Infinitive	Past participle
to hit	hit
to throw	thrown
to ignore	ignored
to call	called
to order	ordered
to laugh	laughed
to damage	damaged
to talk	talked

1 You stupid idiot!

Have you ever ....
someone names? ☐

Why did you do it? ....

....

....

2

Have you ever ....
things at someone? ☐

Why did you do it? ....

....

....

3

Have you ever ....
someone? ☐

Why did you do it? ....

....

....

4

Have you ever ....
someone? ☐

Why did you do it? ....

....

....

5 Toby's so bad at basketball! I know. He's really rubbish.

Have you ever ....
about someone? ☐

Why did you do it? ....

....

....

6

Have you ever ....
at someone? ☐

Why did you do it? ....

....

....

7

Have you ever ....
someone's things? ☐

Why did you do it? ....

....

....

8 Pick up my bag!

Have you ever ....
someone to do something? ☐

Why did you do it? ....

....

....

Learning Styles

How do you learn best? There are three main types of learner.

Complete the sentences for each learning style – choose the correct words from the box.
Tick all the statements that are true for you. Which type of learner are you?
Many people have a mixture of different learning styles.

> interviews, discussions and group work   tapes, the radio or the teacher
> making models and doing experiments   photos, charts and maps
> languages   riding an exercise bike
> the TV or music   sports and dance
> art and design

1 I like studying while I am doing something else, such as ....

2 I'm good at physical subjects, such as ....

3 I like practical work, such as ....

4 I don't like sitting still in lessons. I like to take lots of breaks when I am studying.

Kinesthetic learners learn best by **doing** things.

5 I can't do my homework if there is any noise in the room, such as ....

6 I'm good at visual subjects, such as ....

7 I like learning from books with illustrations, such as ....

8 I remember things best if I write them down.

Visual learners learn best by **seeing** things.

9 I like learning by listening to things, such as ....

10 I'm good at communications subjects, such as ....

11 I like activities with lots of talking, such as ....

12 If I hear something, I will remember it.

Auditory learners learn best by **listening** to things.

Taking Risks

We all need to take risks sometimes. When you take a risk and you are successful,
it makes you more confident. However, some risks are too dangerous or they are illegal.

Look at the risks these fourteen-year-olds would like to take.
Decide if each risk is a good risk or a bad risk.
Complete the sentence with some advice for each person. Use *will* or *might* in your advice.

1 I'd like to fight a boy in my class who bullied me last year.

Good risk ☐ **Bad risk** ☐
If you do this, you will/might ....

2 I'd like to audition for the school play.

Good risk ☐ **Bad risk** ☐
If you do this, you will/might ....

3 I'd like to ring a girl I like and ask her out on a date.

Good risk ☐ **Bad risk** ☐
If you do this, you will/might ....

4 I'd like to go on a school exchange trip to another country.

Good risk ☐ **Bad risk** ☐
If you do this, you will/might ....

5 I'd like to ring some charities to find out about voluntary work.

Good risk ☐ **Bad risk** ☐
If you do this, you will/might ....

6 I'd like to drive my mum's car while she is out.

Good risk ☐ **Bad risk** ☐
If you do this, you will/might ....

7 I'd like to try smoking.

Good risk ☐ **Bad risk** ☐
If you do this, you will/might ....

Everyone is afraid of taking risks. Think of something you would like to do, but are afraid of trying. Complete this form, then decide if the risk is worth taking.

Risk (write what the risk is here)

....
....
....

Why do you want to take this risk?

....
....
....

Write three possible positive results from taking the risk.

....
....
....

Write three possible negative results from taking the risk.

....
....
....

Is the risk worth taking? Why?

....
....
....

Dealing with Danger

Read four stories about teenagers in dangerous situations. Underline the parts of each story that tell you what the characters are saying. Then complete the speech bubbles.

Decide if what each person does is the wrong or right thing to do.

Katie works two evenings a week in a restaurant. One of the customers is a man of about 35. He is always very nice to Katie. One evening Katie tells him that <u>she's nervous about a history test at school</u>. The man says that he would like to take her to dinner and help her study history. Katie tells him that he's very kind. She says that she would love to have dinner with him.

1. I'm nervous about a history test at school.
2.
3.

Is Katie right or wrong?
RIGHT ☐   **WRONG** ☐

Christian is late for his maths lesson. He accidentally bumps into Lucas – the nastiest and most violent boy in the school. Lucas pushes Christian against the wall. Lucas says that Christian needs to buy some new glasses so he can see where he is going. Christian says that he is sorry. Then he walks away.

4.
5.

Is Christian right or wrong?
RIGHT ☐   **WRONG** ☐

Damien is walking home alone late at night. A group of older teenagers stops him. They tell him to give them his wallet. Damien says that he isn't afraid of them. He says that he hasn't got any money on him anyway.

6.
7.

Is Damien right or wrong?
RIGHT ☐   **WRONG** ☐

Isobel is watching TV at home. Her parents and her sisters are out. Suddenly she hears a loud knock on the front door. It is James, her ex-boyfriend, with some of his friends. They have been drinking beer. Isobel knows that James is still angry and upset with her. He didn't want her to end their relationship. James says that he needs to see Isobel. He says that he wants to talk to her. Isobel doesn't open the door. She says that she can't let him in. She says that if he doesn't go away, she will call the police.

8.
9.

Is Isobel right or wrong?
RIGHT ☐   **WRONG** ☐

Are You a Good Friend?

Read the texts. What should each person do?
Complete each sentence with *should* or *shouldn't*.

Fergus asks Stephanie to go out with him on Friday. Stephanie likes Fergus but Stephanie's best friend Karen is Fergus's regular girlfriend. What should Stephanie do?

a She .... tell Karen that Fergus is the wrong boy for her.

b She .... go out with Fergus secretly.

c She .... tell Fergus that she is loyal to Karen and she can't go out with him.

Danny's maths homework is difficult. He wants to copy his friend Jack's homework. Jack doesn't like cheating. What should Jack do?

a He .... tell Danny that he doesn't like cheating.

b He .... let Danny copy his homework.

c He .... say that he has lost his homework.

George's friend Mike went to George's house on Saturday to play computer games. After Mike went home, George couldn't find his favourite game. He thinks that Mike stole it. What should he do?

a He .... go to Mike's house and steal Mike's favourite computer game.

b He .... stop talking to Mike.

c He .... ask Mike what happened.

Are You a Good Friend?

Lucy tells her friend Patrick that her parents are getting divorced. She's very depressed and asks for Patrick's advice. What should Patrick do?

a He .... tell Lucy that everyone has got problems and that she should forget about it.

b He .... listen and tell Lucy that he is happy to talk about it whenever she wants to.

c He .... give Lucy advice about how to help her parents stay together.

Anita and Kylie are good friends. They both love acting and singing. Anita has got the biggest part in the school Christmas show, but Kylie has only got a small part. Kylie is very jealous of Anita. What should Kylie do?

a She .... congratulate Anita and wish her good luck.

b She .... tell everyone that Anita has only got the part because her mother is a teacher at the school.

c She .... tell Anita that she will only be her friend if Anita doesn't act in the show.

Now count your points.

A good friend is loyal. If you are loyal to your friends, they will be loyal to you.

1 a) should 2 shouldn't 3
b) should 0 shouldn't 5
c) should 5 shouldn't 0

A good friend does what they believe is right. Tell your friends if you think that what they are doing is wrong and they will respect you more.

2 a) should 5 shouldn't 0
b) should 0 shouldn't 5
c) should 1 shouldn't 4

A good friend always gives their friends a chance to explain. You don't want friends who are dishonest, but it's no good if you never trust anybody.

3 a) should 0 shouldn't 5
b) should 2 shouldn't 3
c) should 5 shouldn't 0

A good friend is supportive when their friends have problems. If you listen to your friends' problems, they will help you when you have problems.

4 a) should 0 shouldn't 5
b) should 5 shouldn't 0
c) should 2 shouldn't 3

A good friend tries to be happy when their friends are successful. If you say something nice, it will make you feel good, too.

5 a) should 5 shouldn't 0
b) should 0 shouldn't 5
c) should 1 shouldn't 4

Total score

55–70 points
You're a great friend. Friendship is very important to you. You give a lot to your friends.

31–54 points
You're a good friend, but you sometimes make mistakes. Don't worry. Everyone learns from their mistakes.

5–30 points
You need to try harder to be a good friend.

A Roman Villa

**Rich Roman people lived in villas. Here are some of the rooms in a Roman villa.
Rearrange the letters to find the name of each room.**

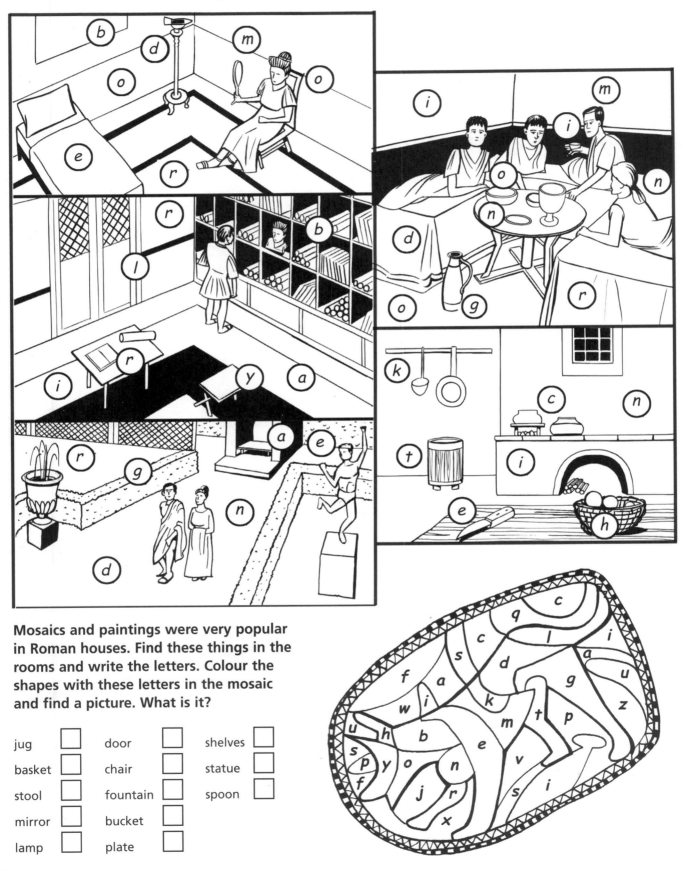

Mosaics and paintings were very popular in Roman houses. Find these things in the rooms and write the letters. Colour the shapes with these letters in the mosaic and find a picture. What is it?

jug	☐	door	☐	shelves	☐		
basket	☐	chair	☐	statue	☐		
stool	☐	fountain	☐	spoon	☐		
mirror	☐	bucket	☐				
lamp	☐	plate	☐				

A Day on the Wagon Train

It is 1843. Your family is one of the first to travel from the east of the United States of America to a new life on the west coast. The journey lasts six months.

This is a typical day on the prairie. Choose the correct verbs and complete the sentences.

(E) find	(I) is	(C) wake up	(R) see
(A) rest	(R) starts	(O) have	(L) cooks
(G) help	(F) washes up	(A) get	(O) walk
(O) puts	(N) sleep	(I) cross	(N) ride

4 a.m.
You (1) ....

4.30 a.m. You (2) .... dressed.
Your mother (3) .... breakfast.

5.30 a.m. Breakfast
(4) .... ready.

6 a.m. Your mother (5) ....
Your father (6) .... the tent in the wagon.

7 a.m. The wagon train
(7) .... moving.
You (8) .... in the wagon.

10 a.m. You (9) ....
a river.

12 noon
You (10) .... for an hour.

1 p.m. You (11) ....
because the wagon is so bumpy. You
(12) .... some Plains Indians.

5 p.m. You (13) ....
a campsite for the night.

6 p.m. You (14) ....
your mother cook supper.

7 p.m. You (15) ....
your lessons.

8 p.m. You (16) ....
in the tent.

Where is the wagon train going? Write the letters next to the verbs in the correct order.

It is going to __ __ __ __ __ __ __ __ __ __ and __ __ __ __ __ __ .
                     1 2 3 4 5 6 7 8 9 10   11 12 13 14 15 16

Space Travel

One of the most important days in the history of space travel: **Apollo 11 lands on the Moon.**

Year: ....

Find 24 words about space and space travel in the wordsearch grid. The letters left over in the grid spell the year of the first landing on the Moon.

Words go across and down.

S	P	A	C	E	S	H	U	T	T	L	E	N	I
P	N	S	E	A	S	T	E	E	E	P	V	N	U
A	S	T	E	R	O	I	D	L	S	L	E	M	R
C	P	R	S	T	L	M	I	E	T	U	N	A	A
E	A	O	G	H	A	O	X	S	A	T	U	R	N
S	C	N	A	N	R	O	T	C	R	O	S	S	U
T	E	A	L	E	S	N	R	O	C	K	E	T	S
A	S	U	A	P	Y	J	U	P	I	T	E	R	Y
T	H	T	X	T	S	A	T	E	L	L	I	T	E
I	I	N	Y	U	T	U	N	I	V	E	R	S	E
O	P	L	A	N	E	T	V	O	Y	A	G	E	R
N	I	N	E	E	M	I	L	K	Y	W	A	Y	■

Write the words here.

S _ _ _ _ _   S _ _ _ _ _ _ _

A S _ _ _ _ _ _ _

S _ T _ _ _ _

R O _ _ _ _ _ _

J U _ _ _ _ _ _

E _ _ _ _ H

N _ P _ _ _ _ _

S _ _ _ _ _   S Y _ _ _ _

M _ O _

V _ Y _ _ _ _

M _ _ _ _   W _ _

S _ _ _ _ _   S T _ _ _ _ _ _

S _ _ _ _ _ S _ _ P

A _ _ _ _ _ N _ _ _ _

G _ _ _ X _

S _ A _

T _ L _ S _ _ _ _

P _ _ _ _ O

V _ _ U _

M _ R _

U _ A _ _ _

S _ T _ _ _ _ _ E

P _ _ _ E _

U _ _ V _ _ _ _

The Incas

The Incas lived in the mountains of South America 500 years ago.
They had a large and powerful empire.

These things, people and places were all very important to the Incas.
Solve the word clues and find the Inca names for these things.

1 The king of the Incas.

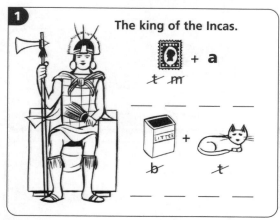

2 A famous Inca city high up in the mountains.

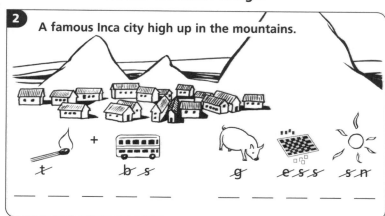

3 The language of the Incas.

4 The mountains where the Incas lived.

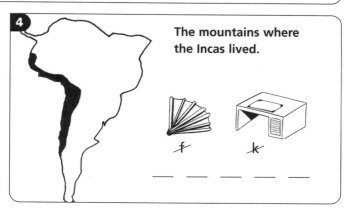

5 The capital city of the Inca empire.

6 The Inca goddess of the earth.

7 The Inca sun god.

The Inuit

**The Inuit have lived in the Arctic for thousands of years.
How did the Inuit keep warm in the freezing Arctic weather?**

**Here are some of the ways they kept warm. Rearrange the words to make sentences.
Put the letters in the correct order to find the Inuktitut word for the things in the pictures.
(Inuktitut is the language of the Inuit.)**

1

(**m**) had   (**a**) Inuit   (**k**) boots
(**k**) The   (**i**) sealskin

....

boots =

....

2

(**a**) wore   (**u**) bear
(**n**) They   (**q**) skins   (**n**) polar

....

polar bear =

....

3

(**g**) houses
(**u**) small   (**l**) were   (**i**) Their

....

house =

....

4

(**l**) homes   (**k**) lamps
(**d**) their   (**u**) heated   (**i**) with   (**k**) They

....

lamp =

....

5

(**u**) hunters   (**i**) made   (**i**) In   (**q**) houses
(**l**) winter   (**g**) temporary   (**a**) snow   (**g**) the

....

snow house =

....

6

(**q**) coats   (**a**) their   (**t**) inside   (**t**) babies
(**i**) young   (**l**) carried   (**u**) women   (**q**) Inuit

....

coat =

....

7

(**a**) ran   (**m**) behind
(**u**) dog   (**q**) Hunters   (**q**) sled   (**t**) the

....

sled =

....

Children in Victorian England

Most children in nineteenth-century England had to work.
Choose the correct answer to each question. Then use the information to find out which job each child does. Write the name of each child under the correct picture.

Ellie
1 Do you live in the country?
Yes, I am. No, I don't.

2 Do you work in a house?
Yes, I can. No, I don't.

Betty
3 Can you read and write?
Yes, I can. No, I'm not.

4 Are you good with children?
Yes, I am. No, I can't.

Georgie
5 Do you work underground?
Yes, I do. No, I'm not.

6 Is your job dangerous?
Yes, it is. No, it hasn't.

Alfie
7 Can you read and write?
Yes, I have. No, I can't.

8 Is your job very dirty?
Yes, it is. No, it doesn't.

a chimney sweep

b flower girl

c textile worker

d seamstress

e farm worker

f pupil teacher

g coal miner

h servant

Cathy
9 Is your job underground?
Yes, it does. No, it isn't.

10 Have you got a uniform?
Yes, I have. No, I don't.

Sarah
11 Is your job very dirty?
Yes, it can. No, it isn't.

12 Are you good at sewing?
Yes, I am. No, I can't.

Sam
13 Do you climb chimneys?
Yes, I have. No, I don't.

14 Is your job in a factory?
Yes, it is. No, it hasn't.

Billy
15 Do you live in a city?
Yes, I am. No, I don't.

16 Do you work with animals?
Yes, I do. No, I haven't.

Here are some laws about children from the nineteenth century.

1842 Children younger than 10 must not work in coal mines.
1847 Children must not work more than 10 hours a day.
1870 All children aged 5–13 must go to school.

Ancient Egyptian Gods and Goddesses

The Ancient Egyptians had many gods. Here are pictures of some of them. Match the small pictures to the correct gods and goddesses to find out what each one was the god or goddess of.

farming	life	babies	magic	dancing	love	writing

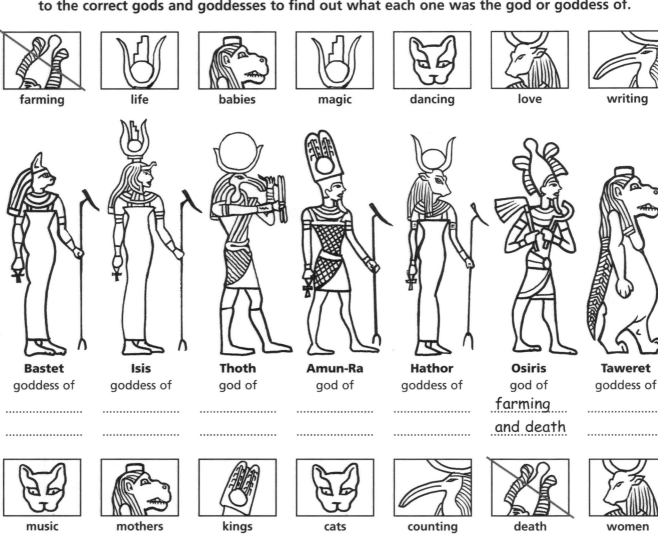

Bastet	**Isis**	**Thoth**	**Amun-Ra**	**Hathor**	**Osiris**	**Taweret**
goddess of	goddess of	god of	god of	goddess of	god of	goddess of
....	....	....	....	....	farming	....
....	....	....	....	....	and death	....

music	mothers	kings	cats	counting	death	women

Find the words for the people in the pictures. Then choose a god or goddess to help each person.

1 ....

2 ....

3 ....

....

....

....

young couple

musician

schoolboy

farmer

mother

pharaoh

4 ....

5 ....

6 ....

....

....

....

Marco Polo

Marco Polo was the first European explorer to visit China. Here are the answers to some questions about his travels. Can you write the questions? Choose the correct beginning to each question and complete the question.

1 ....
....
Marco Polo was a thirteenth-century explorer.

2 ....
....
He was born in Venice in 1254.

3 ....
....
He was 17 years old when he went travelling with his father and uncle.

4 ....
....
They went to China.

5 ....
....
The journey took three and a half years.

6 ....
....
They visited the city of Khanbalik (today called Beijing).

7 ....
....
They met the Emperor of China there.

8 ....
....
Yes, the Emperor liked Marco. (He gave Marco an important job in his court.)

9 ....
....
Marco saw amazing things in China: fireworks, paper money, coal fires and printed books.

10 ....
....
He left China in 1292. (He had been there nearly 20 years.)

How long ...	Ⓐ	Who did ...	Ⓚ
What did ...	Ⓐ	Who was ...	Ⓚ
How old ...	Ⓑ	Where did ...	Ⓛ
Did ...	Ⓗ	When did ...	Ⓝ
Which city ...	Ⓘ	Where was ...	Ⓤ

What was the Emperor of China called? If you have written the questions correctly, the letters of his name will be in the correct order.

__ __ __ __ __ __

__ __ __ __ __

Great Women

Here are five great women from the past. Read the clues and complete the grid
with ticks and crosses. A tick is for 'yes' and a cross is for 'no'.

Find out where each woman lived, when she lived and what she did. Write about each woman.

	Greece	Mongolia	America	Persia	Japan	fourth century BC	eighth century AD	eleventh century AD	thirteenth century AD	nineteenth century AD	warrior	helped slaves escape	princess	writer	doctor
Harriet Tubman					✗										
Murasaki Shikibu	✗	✗	✗	✗	✓					✗	✗				
Agnodice					✗										
Zubaidah					✗										
Aiyurak					✗										

Clues

*Murasaki Shikibu was Japanese. She wasn't a warrior and
she didn't live in the nineteenth century.*

*Aiyaruk lived in the thirteenth century. She wasn't a doctor.
She didn't live in America or Persia.*

*Agnodice wasn't a princess or a writer. She lived before
the eleventh century. She wasn't Persian or Mongolian.*

*Harriet Tubman helped slaves to escape. She didn't live
in Greece, Mongolia or Persia. She wasn't alive in the
eighth century AD.*

*Zubaidah was an eighth century princess. She didn't
live in America or Greece.*

The Mongolian woman was a warrior.

The doctor lived in the fourth century BC.

The American woman lived in the nineteenth century AD.

Write about each woman.

1 Harriet Tubman lived in .... in the .... century.

She ....

2 Murasaki Shikibu lived in .... in the .... century.

She ....

3 Agnodice lived in ....

She ....

4 Zubaidah ....

....

5 Aiyurak ....

....

**Here are some facts
about these women.**

**Can you match each
fact to the correct
person?**

1 When she was 15 her
father arranged for
her to get married.
She refused because
she wanted to be a
soldier. She became a
famous general.

2 Her real name was
Amat Al-Aziz. She
was clever and she
loved music and
painting. She was a
very good person.
She built fountains
and rest houses for
pilgirms.

3 She dressed as a man
because women were
not allowed to be
doctors. When she
was alive, women
had to stay at home.

4 She lived in the royal
court and served the
Empress. She wrote
the world's first
novel, *The Tale of
Genji.*

5 She was born a slave
but she escaped
when she was about
28 years old. She
helped to free nearly
900 slaves.

The Race to the South Pole

In 1911, nobody had ever been to the South Pole. The Norwegian, Roald Amundsen and the British Captain, Robert Scott both wanted to be the first to go there.

Read about their journeys to the South Pole. Put the sentences in the correct order. Then write the dates on the map.

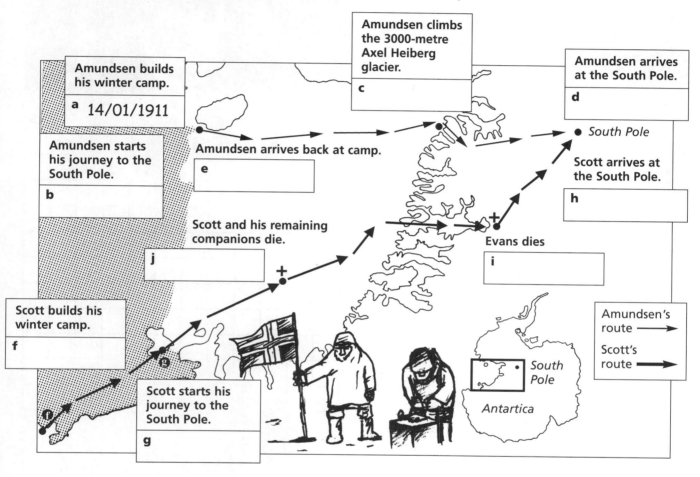

- Amundsen climbs the 3000-metre Axel Heiberg glacier. **c**
- Amundsen builds his winter camp. **a** 14/01/1911
- Amundsen arrives at the South Pole. **d**
- Amundsen starts his journey to the South Pole. **b**
- Amundsen arrives back at camp. **e**
- Scott arrives at the South Pole. **h**
- Scott and his remaining companions die. **j**
- Evans dies **i**
- Scott builds his winter camp. **f**
- Scott starts his journey to the South Pole. **g**
- *South Pole*
- Amundsen's route →
- Scott's route →
- *South Pole*
- *Antartica*

1 On the twentieth of October 1911 Amundsen set out for the South Pole with four companions, four sledges and fifty-two dogs.

2 On the seventeenth of January 1912 Scott reached the South Pole. He saw Amundsen's tent and the Norwegian flag. He knew that he wasn't the first.

3 On the twenty-ninth of March 1912 Scott wrote in his diary for the last time: 'I do not think that I can write more.' He and his companions died in their tent.

4 On the fourteenth of December 1911 Amundsen reached the South Pole. They put up a tent and the Norwegian flag and they left a message for Scott.

5 On the fourteenth of January 1911 Amundsen and his party reached the Bay of Whales. They built their winter camp.

6 On the fourth of January 1911 Scott and his party reached McMurdo Sound. They built their winter hut.

7 On the twenty-seventh of February 1912 Edgar Evans, one of Scott's companions, died.

8 On the seventeenth of November 1911 Amundsen and his party started climbing the 3000-metre Axel Heiberg glacier.

9 On the twenty-fifth of January 1912 Amundsen arrived safely back at his winter camp.

10 On the first of November 1911 Scott and four companions started the long journey to the South Pole. They had sledges pulled by ponies.

Amundsen's expedition

Correct order: ☐ ☐ ☐ ☐ ☐

Scott's expedition

Correct order: ☐ ☐ ☐ ☐ ☐

The Berlin Wall, 1989

The Berlin Wall was built in 1961 to stop East Germans escaping to West Germany.

Read about the end of the Berlin Wall. Read the definitions and find a word in the passage for each definition. Write the words in the grid. Clue: You need to find one word in every sentence.

In October 1989 thousands of East Germans held demonstrations against the Communist government. At 7.30 p.m. on Thursday 9 November, the television news announced that East Germans could now travel to the West. People could get visas to cross the border between East and West Germany. Immediately people gathered at the Berlin Wall. The guards opened the gates and people crowded through the wall to West Berlin. Some people didn't want to wait in the queue so they scaled the wall.

There was a massive party in West Berlin. The West Berliners greeted the East Germans with champagne, cheers and singing. People started hacking at the wall with hammers and chisels. The party lasted all weekend. Many East Germans went shopping in West Berlin – they enjoyed looking at all the goods in the West German shops.

The next day the police started demolishing the wall with bulldozers. It was a momentous day for Germany and for the whole of Europe. It was the end of a divided Germany. It was also the beginning of the end of hostile relationships between East and West Europe.

Definitions

1 very large public meetings
2 line between two countries
3 separated
4 very important
5 pushed
6 cutting and chopping
7 very large
8 continued

9 assembled in groups
10 climbed
11 welcomed
12 unfriendly
13 things for sale
14 said
15 destroying

Now answer these questions.

1 What kind of government ruled East Germany in October 1989?

....

2 What did people have to get to cross the border between East and West Germany?

....

3 Who scaled the wall?

....

4 How did the West Berliners greet the East Germans?

....

5 What did the police do the next day?

....

Samurai Training

The samurai were Japanese warriors. They were the most powerful people in Japan from the 12th to the 18th century.
Read the passage about a samurai's training. Then complete the sentences using these words: *could • couldn't • had to • didn't have to*

Only boys born to samurai parents trained to be samurai. They started school at seven years old. School lasted twelve hours every day. Good manners and obedience were very important. The boys learned to respect their parents and teachers. They also learned reading and writing and how to write poetry, dance and play musical instruments. But the most important lesson was fighting. The sword-master taught the boys how to fight bravely. It was a disgrace to be weak or afraid.

Sometimes girls learned how to fight, but this was very unusual. Most girls stayed at home with their mothers.

The samurai were always right-handed. Left-handed boys learned to use their right hands.

There was no school in the evenings. Boys relaxed and played games with their families.

Some boys became samurai at age 13, some boys couldn't become samurai until they were 14 or 15.

1 Ordinary people .... become samurai. You .... be born in a samurai family.

2 You .... start school at age 7. You .... spend 12 hours a day at school.

3 You .... obey your parents and teachers. You .... be rude to older people.

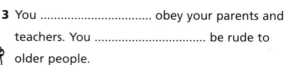

4 You .... learn how to fight with swords. You .... be weak or afraid.

5 Girls .... learn to fight but it was unusual. Most girls .... stay at home with their mothers.

6 You .... be left-handed. You .... learn to use your right hand.

7 In the evenings you .... go to school. You .... play games.

8 You .... become a samurai when you were 13. Some boys .... wait until they were 14 or 15.

This is the commander of the samurai. He was the most powerful man in Japan.
What was he called?
Count how many of each word you used in the exercise.
Write the letters next to the correct numbers to find his title.

	1	2	3	4	5	6	7	8
could	1 th	2 ch	3 sh	4 pl	5 tr	6 sl	7 pr	8 cr
couldn't	1 a	2 ea	3 ie	4 o	5 ou	6 i	7 ai	8 ee
had to	1 f	2 d	3 l	4 r	5 j	6 k	7 m	8 g
didn't have to	1 un	2 ut	3 an	4 at	5 on	6 ot	7 en	8 et

This is the

....

The Vikings

For 300 years in the ninth, tenth and eleventh centuries, the Vikings terrified people in Europe.

Which of these sentences about Vikings are true and which are false?
The sentences with verbs in the wrong tense are false. Find the false sentences
and correct the verbs. Then find the answer for each sentence.
Put the letters next to the answers in the correct order to find where the Vikings lived.

1 All Viking men are fierce warriors and raiders.

2 The Vikings hated cowards.

3 In years with a bad harvest, the Vikings only gave food to strong people.

4 The Vikings discovered America.

5 Viking women fight in battles.

6 Most Vikings believe in Christianity.

7 The Vikings have excellent schools.

8 The Vikings loved listening to stories.

9 Most Vikings can read and write.

10 The Vikings bury important people in castles.

11 The Vikings had slaves.

(N) **False.** The Vikings didn't have schools. Children had to work.

(D) **False.** Viking women worked at home. They cooked and made cloth.

(S) **False.** Most Vikings were peaceful farmers, merchants and craftspeople.

(I) **False.** The Vikings were pagans. They had many gods: for example, Odin, Thor and Freyr.

(I) **False.** The Vikings buried important people in ships or in graves that were in the shape of a ship.

(V) **False.** The Vikings had an alphabet, called Runes, but not many people could write.

(A) **True.** The stories were called sagas. Sagas about the gods and battles were very popular.

(C) **True.** Bravery was very important to the Vikings. If a man died in battle, his family was very proud of him. If he died at home in his bed, they were ashamed of him.

(A) **True.** The Vikings captured slaves when they raided other countries.

(A) **True.** When there wasn't enough food for everybody, the Vikings didn't feed old or sick people.

(N) **True.** In about 1000, Leif Eriksson sailed to the east coast of America.

The Vikings lived in __ __ __ __ __ __ __ __ __ __ __ __ .

Martin Luther King Jr

Dr Martin Luther King Jr was the greatest leader of the American civil rights movement. He fought for equal rights for black people.

Martin Luther King Jr was born in 1929 in Atlanta, in the south of the USA. He grew up with racial segregation. White and black people had different schools and churches. Black people had to live with racism every day.

The bus boycott

In 1964, Martin Luther King Jr became minister of a church in Montgomery, Alabama. The buses in Montgomery were racially segregated. Black people sat at the back and white people sat at the front. If the bus was full, black people had to give their seats to white people.

On 1st December 1955, a woman called Rosa Parks refused to stand up when some white people got on the bus. The police came and arrested her. The black community was very angry.

Dr King organised a bus boycott. All the black people stopped travelling on the buses. People walked to work or travelled by car or taxi. They asked the mayor of Montgomery for three things:

1. Bus drivers must be polite to black passengers.
2. Black people must have the same right to sit down as white people.
3. The bus company must employ black drivers.

The mayor of Montgomery refused the demands and the bus boycott continued for a whole year.

Dr King received letters from the Ku Klux Klan and other white racist groups. They threatened to kill him. One day a racist group bombed Dr King's house. Luckily his wife, Coretta, and their baby were not hurt.

On 13th November 1956 the United States Supreme Court decided that segregation on the buses was illegal. It was a great victory for the black community in Montgomery. It was also the beginning of the civil rights movement in America.

Complete the sentences with these words: *who, that, where.* Use *who* whenever it is possible. Then do the crossword. Find the answers in the story about Martin Luther King Jr.

1 The people .... arrested Mrs Parks.

2 The name of the woman .... was married to Martin Luther King Jr.

3 A person .... drives a bus.

4 The surname of the woman .... refused to stand up on the bus.

5 The protest .... Dr King organised was called the 'bus ....'.

6 The town .... Dr King lived.

7 A person .... is the leader of a church.

8 The town .... Dr King was born.

9 One of the kinds of transport .... people used during the bus boycott.

10 The country .... Martin Luther King Jr lived.

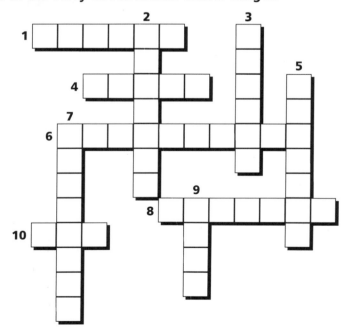

The Twentieth Century

Follow the maze and complete the sentences. Find the dates of famous events in the twentieth century. Colour the arrows that make the correct sentences.

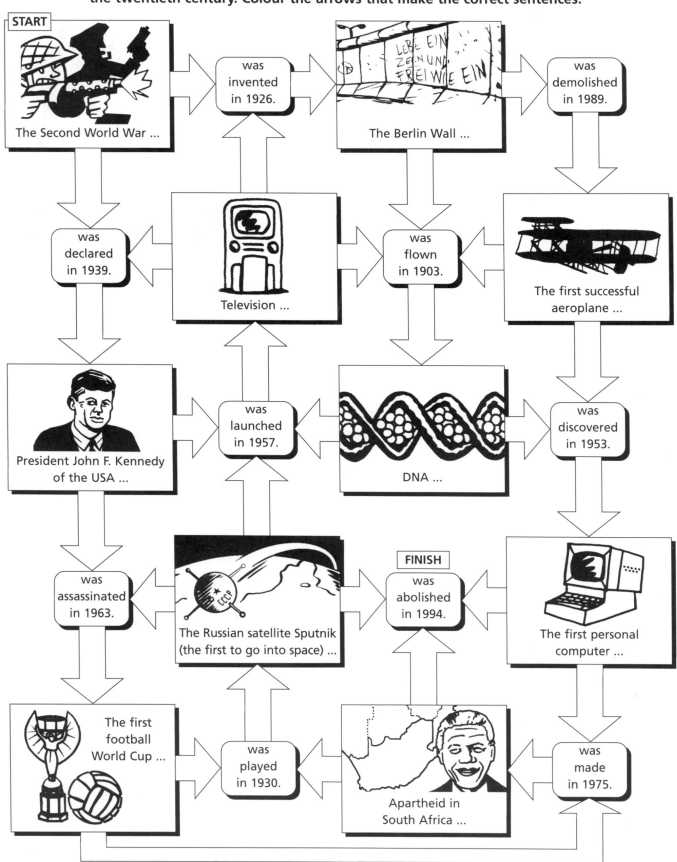

START

The Second World War ...

was invented in 1926.

The Berlin Wall ...

was demolished in 1989.

was declared in 1939.

Television ...

was flown in 1903.

The first successful aeroplane ...

President John F. Kennedy of the USA ...

was launched in 1957.

DNA ...

was discovered in 1953.

was assassinated in 1963.

The Russian satellite Sputnik (the first to go into space) ...

FINISH
was abolished in 1994.

The first personal computer ...

The first football World Cup ...

was played in 1930.

Apartheid in South Africa ...

was made in 1975.

Answers

GEOGRAPHY

Page 4
Flags
A. Jamaica: yellow, black, green B. Canada: red, white
C. South Africa: red, yellow, black, green, blue
D. Sweden: yellow, blue E. Pakistan: white, green
F. Ireland: green, white, orange

Page 5
Regions of the World
Where does it come from?
North America: wheat, oranges
Caribbean: bananas, sugar
South America: coffee, beef
Africa: peanuts, cocoa
Europe: potatoes, cheese
Asia: rice, tea
Oceania: lamb, wine

Pages 6 & 7
Ecosystems
What is it? What does it eat?
1. penguin (i) 2. scorpion (a) 3. mountain goat (g)
4. alligator (b) 5. parrot (h) 6. rabbit (f) 7. dolphin (d)
8. giraffe (c) 9. squirrel (e)
Where does it live?
1. parrot 2. dolphin 3. penguin 4. alligator 5. squirrel
6. scorpion 7. giraffe 8. mountain goat 9. rabbit

Page 8
Recycling
1. metal and chemicals 2. glass 3. cotton 4. paper
5. plastic 6. metal 7. cardboard 8. wool 9. wood
The only material you can't recycle is **plastic**.

Page 9
Geographical Features
1. mountain 2. sea 3. lake 4. wind farm 5. town
6. forest 7. island 8. hill 9. farm 10. coast 11. road
12. bridge 13. river 14. marsh

Pages 10 & 11
World Time Zones
1. seven 2. Madrid 3. nine 4. four 5. Anchorage
6. Chicago 7. Wellington 8. Moscow 9. eight 10. Sydney
11. Cairo 12. Tokyo
The mystery city is **San Francisco**.
The time in this city is **four a.m.**

Page 12
Country Fact File
A. **Russia:** 1. False: This is the **biggest** country in the world.
   2. True.
B. **China:** 3. False: This country is in **Asia**. 4. True.
C. **Tunisia:** 5. True. 6. False: Its coast is on the
   Mediterranean Sea.

D. **Argentina:** 7. False: The capital city is **Buenos Aires**.
   8. True.
E. **Canada:** 9. True. 10. False: This country has the **longest**
   coastline in the world.
F. **Switzerland:** 11. True. 12. False: Most of this country is
   in the **Alps**.
G. **Mexico:** 13. False: The people in this country speak
   Spanish. 14. True.
H. **Kenya:** 15. False: This country is on the **Equator / in
   Africa**. 16. True.
I. **Australia:** 17. True. 18. False: Most of this country is
   desert.
J. **Nepal:** 19. False: This country is surrounded by **land**.
   20. True.

This is a map of **Italy**.

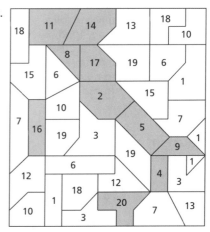

Page 13
Migration
Reasons to emigrate from a region: 1, 5, 6, 8
Reasons to immigrate into a region: 2, 3, 4, 7

	I	N	D	I	A	N		C	H	I	N	E	S	E
N	I	G	E	R	I	A	N		I	R	A	Q	I	
	T	U	R	K	I	S	H		F	R	E	N	C	H
P	O	L	I	S	H		E	G	Y	P	T	I	A	N
		P	O	R	T	U	G	U	E	S	E			
B	R	A	Z	I	L	I	A	N		G	R	E	E	K
	J	A	M	A	I	C	A	N		T	H	A	I	
		B	A	N	G	L	A	D	E	S	H	I		
E	T	H	I	O	P	I	A	N		I	R	I	S	H

Page 14
European Weather
The correct symbols and temperatures are:

Bergen: 12° C
Moscow: 22° C   Budapest:
London: Athens:
Madrid: 25° C   Ankara: 27° C
Warsaw: 18° C

Page 15
Town Planning
Several designs are possible. Students should fill in the gaps with their own choice of buildings.

Page 16
World Travel
1. heard 2. flown 3. ridden 4. seen 5. swum 6. driven 7. taken 8. bought 9. eaten 10. met.
Kirsty and Tim have done 1, 6, 7, 9, 10

Page 17
Earthquakes
1–2.9 B   3–3.9 F   4–4.9 E   5–5.9 C   6–6.9 D   7–9 A
The correct order of events is:
1. Find out how bad the damage is.
2. Rescue people who are trapped under buildings.
3. Provide emergency medical assistance.
4. Provide emergency food, water and shelter.
5. Demolish dangerous buildings.
6. Repair communications.
7. Start rebuilding houses.
8. Start an earthquake education programme.

Page 18
Tourism
Incorrect sentences: B haven't got lot of, C many, M much, O many, E much, U a lot of/many, S much.
The popular holiday country is **Thailand**.

Page 19
Water crossword

MATHS

Page 20
Multiplication

These are suggested answers.
Across
B Eight multiplied by eight.
M Six multiplied by nine.
N Eleven multiplied by nine.
Down
C Six multiplied by seven.
I Nineteen multiplied by five.

Page 21
Averages
running 4   swimming 6   tennis 3   hockey 2   football 5
volleyball 5   gymnastics 2   basketball 3
The most popular sport is **swimming**

Page 22
Fractions
The order of the fractions is: 3/8, 1/4, 3/16, 1/8, 1/16
1. 2500, **2.** 3750, **3.** 1250, **4.** 5000, **5.** 7500

Page 23
Coordinates
(1, 8) church   (4, 2) castle   (2, 4) theatre
(8, 8) swimming pool   (9, 6) library   (5, 7) café
(1, 1) supermarket   (9, 2) doctor's
The **shopping centre** is at (6,2)

Page 24
Division Directions
The correct order of sums and the answers are:
$63 \div 7 = 9$; $32 \div 8 = 4$; $45 \div 9 = 5$;
$64 \div 8 = 8$; $24 \div 4 = 6$; $7 \div 7 = 1$;
$33 \div 11 = 3$; $16 \div 8 = 2$; $84 \div 12 = 7$;
$100 \div 10 = 10$
Finish at **D**.

Page 25
Factors and Multiples
A. 60; **B.** 7; **C.** 30; **D.** 24; **E.** 4; **F.** 12; **G.** 52
a) 60, b) 24, c) 7, d) 30, e) 52, f) 12 g) 4

Page 26
Ordering Numbers
1. The young couple and their baby live in flat four.
   157, 286, 329, 364, 491, 538, 635, 812, 870, 943
2. Between the elderly lady and the young man there is a family of four.
   0.0065, 0.035, 0.175, 0.536, 0.563, 0.783, 1.573, 1.742, 3.184, 6.571, 7.196, 31.48, 56.23, 75.12
3. The middle-aged couple live above the young man.
   5.765, 5.867, 5.876, 6.857, 7.586, 7.856, 8.675, 8.756
4. The young couple and their baby live next to the three flatmates.
   −9.35, −8.29, −7.51, −7.051, −5.76, −1.82, 0, 0.84, 1.32, 2.45, 6.92, 9.63
Flat 1: June Willis;
Flat 2: the Andersons;
Flat 3: James Nichols;
Flat 4: the Peels
Flat 5: Sally Preston, Claire Sanchez and Mark Osborne;
Flat 6: Candice and George Sweet.

Page 27
Equivalent Fractions
1. The jester was singing a song.
   (2/3 = 4/6 = 10/15 = 20/30)
2. The cook was baking some cakes.
   (5/8 = 10/16 = 15/24 = 20/32)

3. The laundry maid was ironing the clothes.
   (2/5 = 6/15 = 8/20 = 14/35)
4. The butler was stealing the crown.
   (1/5 = 2/10 = 4/20 = 5/25)
5. The coachman was feeding the horses.
   (4/7 = 8/14 = 40/70 = 20/35)
6. The kitchen maid was washing the floor.
   (3/4 = 6/8 = 12/16 = 21/28)
It was the **butler**.

Page 28
Maths Millionaire
Percentages: b) 5, c) 36, b) 208.8, a) 650
Fractions: b) 4/7, c) 1/8, c) 2, a) 4/8
Number sequences: a) 11, c) 128, c) 35, b) 95
Fractions, percentages and decimals: a) 1/2, b) 0.75,
c) 86%, b) 3/5
Mental arithmetic: b) 100, b) 92, a) 8, c) 288

Page 29
Percentages
SUPER SHOP: 1. Dresses £17.50; 2. Jackets £50;
                     3. T-shirts £12.50; 4. Jumpers £18
COOL CLOTHES: 5. Shoes £30; 6. Jeans £24;
                     7. Jackets £45; 8. T-shirts £12
GARAGE: 9. Jumpers £14; 10. Dresses £21;
                     11. Skirts £17.50; 12. Coats £45.50
FIRST FASHION: 13. Shoes £32; 14. T-shirts £10;
                     15. Jeans £22.50; 16. Jumpers £20
a. True; **b.** False; **c.** False; **d.** False; **e.** True; **f.** True

Pages 30 & 31
Cubes
A. yes; **B.** no; **C.** no; **D.** yes; **E.** no; **F.** no **G.** yes; **H.** yes

Page 32
Negative Numbers
−1 + 2 = 1 (quickly), −6 + 6 = 0 (untidily), 4 − 7 = −3 (well),
−6 − 4 = −10 (terribly), −11 + 7 = −4 (messily),
−7 x −2 = 14 (clumsily), −10 x 5 = −50 (early),
−12 x −3 = 36 (carefully)
1. bad at, **2.** good at, **3.** good at, **4.** good at, **5.** bad at,
6. bad at, **7.** good at, **8.** bad at

Page 33
Shapes

H	e	'	s		n	e	i	t	h	e	r
t	a	l	l		n	o	r		f	a	t.
H	e	'	s		w	e	a	r	i	n	g
e	i	t	h	e	r		j	e	a	n	s
o	r		a		T	-	s	h	i	r	t
b	u	t		n	o	t		b	o	t	h.

It is boy **d**.

Page 34
Equations
1. (x) am watching, (y) watched; coordinate: (3,6)
   (x) bought, (y) am going to buy; coordinate: (1,2)
   equation: y = 2x

2. (x) played, (y) am going to play; coordinate: (-1,-4)
   (x) did, (y) am doing; coordinate: (3,0)
   equation: y = x −3

3. (x) am taking, (y) am going to take; coordinate: (-3,-2)
   (x) am going to go, (y) went; coordinate: (4,5)
   equations: y = x + 1

Page 35
Decimals
1. **6.65** False, 2. **25.359** False, 3. **18.78** False, 4. **60** True,
5. **2.22** False, 6. **287.21** True, 7. **76.79** False, 8. **0.646** True,
9. **0.3792** True, 10. **10.675** True, 11. **3.7576** True,
12. **78.76** False
A. Suzanne, **B.** Julie, **C.** Kylie, **D.** Tina, **E.** Anna, **F.** Leanne.

Pages 36 & 37
Theme Park Arithmetic
ENTRANCE: It should cost **£38**
VISITORS: There should be **52 million** visitors every year.
JOB OPPORTUNITIES: Fun World should have a total of
144 employees.
DARTS: The girl should win a **small teddy**.
WATERFALL: It should cost **£12.50**
FUN WORLD FOOD: It should cost **£5.90**
BIGGEST ROLLERCOASTER IN THE WORLD: The ride should
last **3** minutes.
LOTTERY: The boy should win **£10**
SOUVENIR SHOP: The **baseball cap** should be free.

Page 38
Word Calculations
big (18) big-headed; long (48) long-winded; hard (31)
hard-working; kind (38) kind-hearted; back (17) back-
breaking; tight (64) tight-fisted; computer (111) computer-
literate; quick (61) quick-witted; bad (7) bad-tempered;
home (41) homemade
4. back-breaking; 16. big-headed; 36. computer-literate;
40. bad-tempered; 88. kind-hearted; 104. homemade;
120. tight-fisted; 184. hard-working; 276. long-winded;
391. quick-witted

SCIENCE

Page 39
Sleep
1. twenty-eight years old; **2.** two and a half years old;
3. sixty-one years old; **4.** five months old;
5. eighteen years old; **6.** seven and a half years old;
7. two months old; **8.** forty-three years old

Pages 40 & 41
Dinosaurs
1. a) fast, b) small, c) thin, d) long
2. a) enormous, b) thin, c) short, d) long
3. a) huge, b) heavy, c) small, d) long
4. a) big, b) strong, c) small, d) sharp

Which dinosaur is it?
1. fat, 2. small, 3. short, 4. long. It's a **Stegosaurus**.

Page 42
Bones
1. head,
2. nose,
3. shoulder,
4. neck,
5. chest,
6. arm,
7. hand,
8. back,
9. hip,
10. knee,
11. foot.

This is a
skeleton.

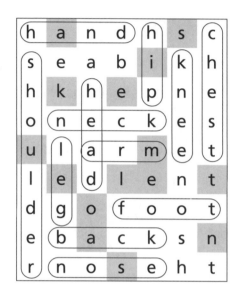

Page 43
The Solar System
1f) Mercury, 2a) Earth, 3d) Jupiter, 4c) Saturn,
5e) Pluto, 6b) Venus
The biggest comet in the Solar System is called **Chiron**.

Pages 44 & 45
Technology
1M 2I 3C 4R 5O 6C 7H 8I 9P
The answer is **microchip**

Page 46
Memory
Students' own answers

Page 47
Senses

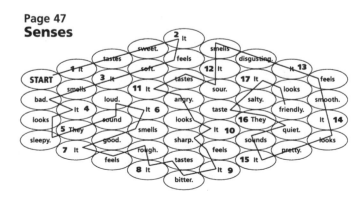

Page 48
The pH Scale
0. dark pink, **1.** pink, **2.** red, **3.** orange, **4.** light orange,
5. pale orange, **6.** yellow, **7.** pale green, **8.** light green,
9. green, **10.** dark green, **11.** pale blue, **12.** light blue,
13. dark blue, **14.** purple
a) more, b) more, c) less, d) less, e) less.
Water has a pH number of 7.

Page 49
Food Web
1. Yes, they do. **2.** No, it isn't. **3.** No, they aren't.
4. Yes, they can. **5.** Yes, they are. **6.** No, they haven't.
7. Yes, they can. **8.** Yes, they are. **9.** No, they don't.
10. Yes, they can. **11.** Yes, they have. **12.** Yes, they do.
13. No, they can't. **14.** Yes, they do. **15.** Yes, they are.

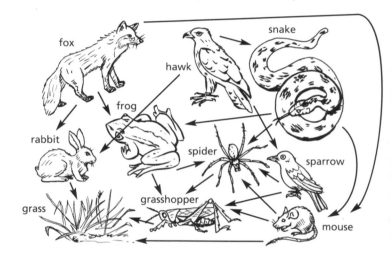

Page 50
Energy Crossword

The answer is
power station

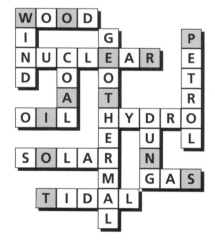

Page 51
The Human Body
1. The **brain controls** the body.
2. The lungs **take** oxygen from the **air**.
3. The **heart** pumps **blood** around the body.
4. The stomach **digests** food.
5. The **skin protects** the body from damage and **disease**.
6. The **kidneys filter** waste products from blood.
7. Nerves **carry information** to and from the brain.
8. Blood carries oxygen and **food** to the **cells**.

Page 52
Predicting the Future
Students' own answers

Page 53
Animal Groups
1. Living, 2. Hunting, 3. Barking, 4. Marking, 5. Keeping,
6. Raising, 7. Howling.
How animals act when they are together is called
animal behaviour.

Page 54
Weight
1. 22.2 kilos, 2. 94.4 kilos, 3. 56 kilos, 4. 63.7 kilos,
5. 26.4 kilos, 6. 8 kilos.
Weight on the sun = 270.7 kilos

LIFE SKILLS

Page 55
Who are you?
Students' own answers.

Page 56
Fruit and Vegetables
1. grapes, 2. pepper, 3. strawberry, 4. tomato, 5. potatoes,
6. banana 7. orange 8. carrots, 9. sweetcorn 10. beans

Page 57
Girls and Boys
Students' own answers.

Pages 58 & 59
Which Job?
1f, 2d, 3i, 4m, 5b, 6l, 7a,
8o, 9j, 10e, 11g, 12h, 13k,
14n, 15c

b) a hairdresser

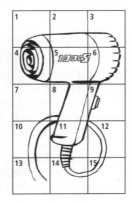

Page 60
A Healthy Life
1. fruit and vegetables; 2. smoke; 3. nine; 4. breakfast;
5. water; 6. sports; 7. stairs; 8. Walk or cycle; 9. shower;
10. one hour; 11. drugs; 12. milk; 13. outside;
14. in the park; 15. in the sun

Page 61
Saving money
Students' own answers.

Page 62
How do you feel?
1. nervous, 2. lonely, 3. sad, 4. upset, 5. tired, 6. free,
7. annoyed, 8. happy, 9. angry, 10. scared, 11. hungry,
12. excited

Page 63
Summer Plans
Students' own answers.

Page 64
Making Conversation
1i, 2f, 3g, 4a, 5e, 6b, 7h, 8d, 9c The word is **hi**

Page 65
Babysitting
Suggested answers:
You shouldn't let the children watch scary programmes on
    television.
You should stop the children fighting.
You should move the cup of hot coffee out of reach of the
    children.
You should move the candle out of reach of the children.
You should move the matches out of reach of the children.
You should move the plates and glasses to a place where
    they won't be knocked over.
You should put the medicine bottle and the pills in a very
    safe place, preferably a cupboard or cabinet high up
    on a wall.
You should tidy away the toys that are all over the floor.
You should close the window.
You should turn the music down.
You should watch the children.
You shouldn't smoke when you're with the children.

Page 66
Summer Jobs
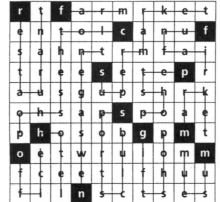

1. farm
2. clothes shop
3. office
4. hotel
5. newsagent
6. supermarket
7. funfair
8. pet shop
9. sports club
10. gift shop
11. market
12. museum

a) clothes shop, b) museum, c) funfair, d) office,
e) sports club, f) pet shop

Page 68
Bullying
1. called, 2. thrown, 3. hit, 4. ignored, 5. talked,
6. laughed, 7. damaged, 8. ordered.
Students' own answers.

Page 69
Learning Styles
1. riding an exercise bike; 2. sports and dance;
3. making models and doing experiments
5. the TV or music; 6. art and design;
7. photos, charts and maps
9. tapes, the radio or the teacher; 10. languages;
11. interviews, discussions and group work
Students' own answers.

Page 70
Taking Risks
Students' own answers with advice and guidance
from the teacher.

Page 71
Dealing with Danger
2. **Customer:** I'd like to take you to dinner
and help you study history.

3. **Katie:** You're very kind. I'd love to
have dinner with you.

4. **Lucas:** You need to buy some new glasses
so you can see where you're going.

5. **Christian:** I'm sorry.

6. **Teenagers:** Give us your wallet!

7. **Damien:** I'm not afraid of you. I haven't got
any money on me.

8. **James:** Isobel, I need to see you. I want to
talk to you.

9. **Isobel:** I can't let you in. If you don't go away,
I'll call the police.

Students' own answers with advice and guidance
from the teacher.

Pages 72 & 73
Are you a Good Friend?
The answers are on page 73.

HISTORY

Page 74
A Roman Villa
bedroom, library, garden, dining room, kitchen
jug (g), basket (h), stool (y), mirror (m), lamp (d), door (l),
chair (o), fountain (r), bucket (t), plate (n), shelves (b),
statue (e), spoon (k)
The mosaic picture is a dog.

Page 75
A Day on the Wagon Train
1. wake up, 2. get, 3. cooks, 4. is, 5. washes up, 6. puts,
7. starts, 8. ride, 9. cross, 10. rest, 11. walk, 12. see,
13. find, 14. help, 15. have, 16. sleep
It is going to **California** and **Oregon.**

Page 76
Space Travel
Space Shuttle, asteroid, Saturn, rockets, Jupiter, Earth,
Neptune, Solar System, Moon, Voyager, Milky Way, space
station, spaceship, astronaut, galaxy, star, telescope, Pluto,
Venus, Mars, Uranus, satellite, planet, universe
Year: Nineteen sixty nine

Page 77
The Incas
1. stamp, bin, cat: Sapa Inca
2. match, bus, pig, chess, sun: Machu Pichu
3. queen, church: Quechua
4. fan, desk: Andes
5. cup, zip, cow: Cuzco
6. pan, chair, man, map: Pacha Mama
7. pin, tiger: Inti

Page 78
The Inuit
1. The Inuit had sealskin boots. *kamik*
2. They wore polar bear skins. *nanuq*
3. Their homes were small. *iglu*
4. They heated their homes with lamps. *kudlik*
5. In the winter hunters made temporary snow houses.
igluigaq
6. Inuit women carried young babies inside their coats.
qulittaq
7. Hunters ran behind the dog sled. *qamtuq*

Page 79
Children in
Victorian England
1. No, I don't. 2. No, I don't. 3. Yes, I can. 4. Yes, I am.
5. Yes, I do. 6. Yes, it is. 7. No, I can't. 8. Yes, it is.
9. No, it isn't. 10. Yes, I have. 11. No, it isn't. 12. Yes, I am.
13. No, I don't. 14. Yes, it is. 15. No, I don't. 16. Yes, I do.
a) Alfie, b) Ellie, c) Sam, d) Sarah, e) Billy, f) Betty,
g) Georgie, h) Cathy

Page 80
Ancient Egyptian gods
and goddesses
Bastet: goddess of cats, dancing and music
Isis: goddess of magic and life
Thoth: god of writing and counting
Amun-Ra: god of kings
Hathor: goddess of love and women
Osiris: god of death and farming
Taweret: goddess of mothers and babies

1. schoolboy: Thoth; 2. mother: Taweret;
3. young couple: Hathor; 4. farmer: Osiris;
5. pharaoh: Amun-Ra; 6. musician: Bastet

Page 81
Marco Polo
1. Who was Marco Polo?
2. Where was he born?
3. How old was Marco when he went travelling?
4. Where did they go?

5. How long did the journey take?
6. Which city did they visit?
7. Who did they meet there?
8. Did the Emperor like Marco?
9. What did Marco see in China?
10. When did Marco leave China?

Kublai Khan

Page 82
Great Women

1. Harriet Tubman lived in America in the nineteenth century. She helped slaves to escape.
2. Murasaki Shikibu lived in Japan in the eleventh century. She was a writer.
3. Agnodice lived in Greece in the fourth century BC. She was a doctor.
4. Zubaidah lived in Persia in the eighth century. She was a princess.
5. Aiyurak lived in Mongolia in the thirteenth century. She was a warrior.

Facts: 1. Aiyurak, **2.** Zubaidah, **3.** Agnodice, **4.** Murasaki Shikibu, **5.** Harriet Tubman

Page 83
The Race to the South Pole

Amundsen's expedition: 5, 1, 8, 4, 9
Scott's expedition: 6, 10, 2, 7, 3
a) 14/01/1911, b) 20/10/1911, c) 17/11/1911, d) 14/12/1911,
e) 25/01/1912, f) 04/01/1911, g) 01/11/1911, h) 17/01/1912,
i) 27/02/1912, j) 29/03/1912

Page 84
The Berlin Wall, 1989

1. a Communist government
2. They had to get visas.
3. People who didn't want to wait in a queue.
4. With champagne, cheers and singing.
5. They started demolishing the wall with bulldozers.

Page 85
Samurai training

1. couldn't, had to **2.** had to, had to **3.** had to, couldn't
4. had to, couldn't **5.** could, had to **6.** couldn't, had to
7. didn't have to, could **8.** could, had to
could (3), couldn't (4), had to (8), didn't have to (1): **shogun**

Page 86
The Vikings

1. (S) False (were). Most Vikings were peaceful farmers, merchants and craftspeople.
2. (C) True. Bravery was very important to the Vikings. If a man died in battle, his family was very proud of him. If he died at home in his bed, they were ashamed of him.
3. (A) True. When there wasn't enough food for everybody, the Vikings didn't feed old or sick people.
4. (N) True. In about 1000, Leif Eriksson sailed to the east coast of America.
5. (D) False (fought). Viking women worked at home. They cooked and made cloth.
6. (I) False (believed). The Vikings were pagans. They had many gods: for example, Odin, Thor and Freyr.
7. (N) False (had). The Vikings didn't have schools. Children had to work.
8. (A) True. The stories were called sagas. Sagas about the gods and battles were very popular.
9. (V) False (could). The Vikings had an alphabet, called Runes, but not many people could write.
10. (I) False (buried). The Vikings buried important people in ships or in graves that were in the shape of a ship.
11. (A) True. The Vikings captured slaves when they raided other countries.

The Vikings lived in Scandinavia.

Page 87
Martin Luther King Jr

1. who
2. who
3. who
4. who
5. that
6. where
7. who
8. where
9. that
10. where

Page 88
The Twentieth Century

The correct order of sentences is:
1. The Second World War was declared in 1939.
2. President John F. Kennedy of the USA was assassinated in 1963.
3. The first football World Cup was played in 1930.
4. The Russian satellite Sputnik was launched in 1957.
5. Television was invented in 1926.
6. The Berlin Wall was demolished in 1989.
7. The first successful aeroplane was flown in 1903.
8. DNA was discovered in 1953.
9. The first personal computer was made in 1975.
10. Apartheid in South Africa was abolished in 1994.

All of our photocopiable resource books are listed below.
Free sample pages can be downloaded from the Teacher's section of our website:
www.link2english.com

PRIMARY

Crazy Pictures

Get the Picture

JET Primary Teachers' Resource Book 1

JET Primary Teachers' Resource Book 2

JET Primary Teachers' Resource Book 3

Kids Only Songbook & Cassette 1 (1997/98 – purple)

Kids Only Songbook & Cassette 2 (1998/99 – green)

Kids Only Songbook & Cassette 3 (1999/00 – red)

Kids Only Songbook & Cassette 4 (2000/01 – yellow)

Start With a Song

SECONDARY

Timesaver Plays

Timesaver Festivals and Special Days in Britain

Timesaver Holidays and Special Days in the USA

Timesaver Cross-curricular English Activities

Timesaver Grammar Activities (Elementary)

Timesaver Vocabulary Activities (Elementary)

Timesaver Games

New Timesavers

Material written by: Melanie Birdsall

Commissioning Editor: Emma Grisewood

Content Editor: Cheryl Pelteret

Designer: Christine Cox

Cover photo: Christopher Woods

Cover Design: Kaya Cully

Illustrations by: Chris Watson & Neale Thomas

© Mary Glasgow Magazines,
an imprint of Scholastic Inc., 2001

All rights reserved.

Printed in the UK by The Baskerville Press Ltd.

Salisbury, Wiltshire.